Foundations for Algebra: Year 2

Managing Editors:

Elizabeth Coyner
    Bear River School
Beverly Brockhoff
    Glen Edwards Middle School

Illustrator:

Jonathan Weast
    Weast & Weast Illustration Studio
    Sacramento, California

Technical Assistance:

Bethany Sorbello
    CPM Educational Program
Thu Pham
    The CRESS Center
    University of California, Davis

Developed by CPM Educational Program

Program Directors:

Judith Kysh
    Departments of Mathematics and Education
    San Francisco State University
Tom Sallee
    Department of Mathematics
    University of California, Davis
Brian Hoey
    CPM Educational Program

v 3.0

Credits for the First Edition

Substantially Revised (2000, 2001)
by

Heidi Ackley
Steve Ackley
Elizabeth Baker
Bev Brockhoff
Ellen Cafferata
Elizabeth Coyner
Sara Effenbeck
William Funkhouser
Brian Hoey
Carol Jancsi

Judy Kysh
Kris Petersen
Robert Petersen
Edwin Reed
Stacy Rocklein
Kristie Sallee
Tom Sallee
Howard Webb
Kaye Whitney
Jon Wickham

Pilot Edition Contributing Editors (1999)

Heidi Ackley
Steve Ackley
Bev Brockhoff
Ellen Cafferata
Elizabeth Coyner
Scott Coyner
Kathleen Davies
Merci Del Rosario
Virginia Downing
Sara Effenbeck
Alice Elstien
William Ford

William Funkhouser
Bruce Grip
Stephen Inouye
Carol Jancsi
Alvin Mendle, Jr.
Pattie Montgomery
Edwin Reed
Gail Standiford
Gale Sunderland
Howard Webb
Kaye Whitney
Jon Wickham

Technical Assistance

Jennifer Buddenhagen
Grace Chen
Ankit Jain
Janelle Petersen

Jeremy Tauzer
David Trombly
Erika Wallender
Emily Wheelis

Foundations for Algebra: Year 2
First Edition

Table of Contents

A Note to Parents, Students, and Teachers

Welcome to *Foundations for Algebra: Year 2*.

This textbook will prepare students for future Algebra courses. It was also written to consolidate the core ideas of previous mathematics courses, so that it will serve students of varied mathematics backgrounds. The contents of this course are many of the fundamental ideas and procedures necessary to be successful in subsequent mathematics courses and many careers. Classroom teachers wrote the lessons to present these ideas in ways that have proven successful with their students. The course also meets local, state, and national curriculum standards.

The investigations, problems, and practice exercises are designed to develop the students' logical and mathematical reasoning skills. The sequence of problems leads to understanding the reasoning behind the mathematical concepts. Students complete guided investigations that explore and develop ideas, then practice them along with procedural skills in subsequent chapters. Many problems use the mathematics in situations like those encountered by students and adults in their daily activities and business settings.

In order to be successful in mathematics it is critical that students actively participate in their learning. This means that each student must read and work all of the problems. Students need to discuss mathematical concepts and the reasoning involved in the steps of their solutions. In order to provide these discussion opportunities, students are encouraged to work with a study partner and in study teams both inside and outside the classroom. It is critical that students complete ALL of the assignments, including homework, to develop their individual skills. Equally important is that students take accurate, complete notes and ask questions about any problem, question, or concept that they find confusing or difficult to understand.

There are two additional resources that the authors designed to help students be successful in this course. The first is the mathematics Tool Kit that contains most of the ideas a student needs to know in the course. Tool Kit entries appear in the student text and in a Tool Kit booklet. The other is the *Foundations for Algebra Parent Guide*. The guide is sometimes available from the classroom teacher or the school library. It is available through the Internet at www.cpm.org. It may also be purchased directly from CPM Educational Program for $20 plus $3 shipping (California residents please add local sales tax to the $20) by sending a check to CPM, 1233 Noonan Drive, Sacramento, CA 95822.

Getting Organized

Chapter 1

Chapter 1
Getting Organized: DATA INTERPRETATION

In this course you will build a foundation that will prepare you for algebra and more advanced mathematics. In this chapter you will begin to develop good work habits by becoming better organized and working with a partner or a study team. You will look at ways to <u>organize and analyze data</u> in a variety of graphs. You will begin to develop the problem solving strategy of Guess and Check.

In this chapter you will have the opportunity to:

- develop good work habits with homework.

- become accustomed to working with a partner or in a team.

- prepare your notebook for the course.

- collect, organize, display, and interpret data.

- solve word problems using the Guess and Check strategy as preparation for writing and solving equations.

Read the problem below, but **do not try to solve it now**. What you learn over the next few days will enable you to solve it.

GO-0. Dezzirae's oldest brother Kalani has saved enough money to buy a car. Kalani told Dezzirae, "Buying a car will actually be a good investment. I can buy it now and sell it when I need the money back. Except for buying gas, it will be almost free because I can get all my money back when I sell it."

Dezzirae looked concerned. "Kalani, I think you should collect some information before you make that kind of statement. Investing your money in a car is not a good idea!"

"I don't agree with you, Dezzirae!" Kalani replied.

Collect, organize, and analyze some data to help Dezzirae and Kalani settle their disagreement.

Number Sense	▓░░░░░░░░░░░░░░░░░
Algebra and Functions	▓░░░░░░░░░░░░░░░░░
Mathematical Reasoning	▓▓░░░░░░░░░░░░░░░░
Measurement and Geometry	▓░░░░░░░░░░░░░░░░░
Statistics, Data Analysis, & Probability	▓▓▓▓▓▓▓░░░░░░░░░░

Chapter 1
Getting Organized: DATA INTERPRETATION

GO-1.   You will be working in pairs or teams of four during this year. You will need to be able to work cooperatively with many different people. Working as a team is a valuable skill. Follow your teacher's instructions to interview your partner. Then you will introduce your partner to another pair. This is the first step for creating a good study team.

GO-2.   On the sticky note provided by your teacher, write your name and the month and day of the month you were born (not the year). An example is pictured below. This problem and the next one will investigate the question, "What are the most common birth month and least common birth month in the class?"

Answer the following questions with your partner before taking your sticky note to the line plot your teacher has prepared. Make sure you write your answers in complete sentences.

| Marion |
| April |
| 21 |

a)   Predict which month of the year will have the most birth dates in it.

b)   Predict which month of the year will have the fewest birth dates in it.

c)   Do you think any two people in your class will share the same birth date?

GO-3.   Follow your teacher's directions about how to place your sticky note on the line plot provided for you. After everyone in class has placed their data on the line plot, answer the following questions using complete sentences.

a)   Which month(s) have the most birth dates? How does the class data compare with your prediction?

b)   Which month(s) have the fewest birth dates? How does the class data compare with your prediction?

c)   Are there any pairs of students in your class who share the same birth date? Are you surprised?

d)   Do you think students in other classes like this one will have shared birth dates? Estimate the number of pairs of students with shared birth dates.

e)   Write down a career or job that might require the employee to arrange data in a line plot such as the one you just completed.

GO-4.   **Mathography** A mathography is a lot like your life history, except that it is focused on mathematics in your life.

a)   On a separate piece of paper, write a letter about yourself to your teacher. The letter will help your teacher get to know you as an individual. The letter should address these three general topics: you, you as a student, and you as a math student. Remember to use complete sentences and make sure it is neat enough to be read easily. Start the letter with "Dear ...". Make sure you sign your letter. This should take between fifteen and twenty minutes to complete. Parts (b), (c), and (d) have suggestions for each of the three topics.

b)   **You**: Introduce yourself, using the name you like to be called. Describe your hobbies, talents, and interests. State your goals or dreams. What are you proud of? What else would you like to share?

c)   **You as a Student**: State the importance of school in your life. Describe yourself as a student. In what kinds of classroom activities do you excel? What kinds of activities do you find frustrating? Explain which subject(s) is/are your favorites. Tell why you like it (them). How regularly do you finish in-class assignments? How faithfully do you do your homework?

d)   **You as a Math Student**: Describe your most memorable moment in math and explain why you remember it. State your favorite math topic. Name your least favorite. Explain how you feel about math this year. What grade do you expect to earn?

GO-5.   Describe each situation below with a fraction.

a)   b)   c)

GO-6.   Compute without using a calculator. The icon you see at left under the problem number means to compute without using a calculator.

a)   7.5 + 3.6   b)   9.5 − 3.8   c)   15.4 + 14.6

d)   85.3 − 55.4   e)   4(2.5)   f)   3.5(10)

GO-7.   The purpose of this exercise is to develop the skill of working with others when you may not always agree with their ideas.

a)   Working alone, list two or three of your favorite items in each category.

Soft Drinks   Movies   Sports
Books   Food   Board Games
Ice Cream   School Subjects

b)   When you and your partner have completed your own lists, show them to each other. Your task now is to try to reach agreement on one item for each category as a team "favorite." Your team favorite may not necessarily be your own first choice. Write your agreed upon choice for as many categories as you can and list the one you could not agree on. Be prepared to describe your negotiations to the class.

GO-8. Many students have difficulty taking notes for a math class, so we will make some suggestions to assist you with this study skill. You will keep all of your math notes together in a special place called a Tool Kit.

When it is time to make notes, a Tool Kit icon like the one at left will be printed in the textbook under the problem number. The mathematics information will appear inside a double-lined box. The double-lined box will be printed in two places: in the textbook and in your Tool Kit. Some schools use the bound Tool Kit booklet from CPM; others photocopy the pages and have you put them in a three-ring binder. Next to the double-lined box in your Tool Kit is a place for you to make notes. Sometimes you will write or highlight key words, a phrase, or a list. Other times you will need to write one or more complete sentences. Follow the directions below each Tool Kit problem in the textbook and write neatly so your notes will be useful.

This is your first Tool Kit entry. This information is the first of four study team guidelines.

STUDY TEAM GUIDELINES

1. **Each member of the team is responsible for his or her own behavior.**

Make these notes in your Tool Kit to the right of the double-lined box.

a)   Highlight the words "responsible," "own," and "behavior."

b)   List some behaviors of a student who is following this guideline.

c)   List some behaviors of a student who is not following this guideline.

GO-9. Organization is a key component of success in almost everything you do. You will need to keep an organized binder for this course. Follow the guidelines set by your teacher.

a) You will need a sturdy 3-ring binder with a hard cover.

b) Put your name on the inside front cover of this binder. Divide your binder into labeled sections as directed by your teacher.

c) After you have completed this task, write "I have finished organizing my binder" next to this problem number on your paper for this assignment.

GO-10.

A COMPLETE GRAPH

Graphs are ways of displaying and comparing information. A complete graph has the following characteristics:

• All graphs are **neat** and easy to read and, when appropriate, constructed with a **straightedge**.

• The units (or numbers) along the axes are clearly **labeled**.

• The axes (the vertical and horizontal number lines) are labeled with **words** that explain the numbers on the axes.

• The units (numbers marked on the axes) follow **equal intervals** on each axis.

• All graphs have a **title**.

• A key or **legend** is included when it is necessary to explain any symbols that are used in the graph.

Graphs should be drawn on graph paper or resource pages.

Make these notes in your Tool Kit to the right of the double-lined box.

a) Highlight any characteristics of a complete graph that you have not studied before.

b) Write a question about any characteristics of graphs that you do not understand. Be sure to ask your partner or a teammate for help. If they are unable to help you, ask your teacher.

GO-11.   Use your Tool Kit as a check-off list to help you find what is missing on each graph
          below. When you see the icon at left under the problem number, you will identify and
          correct the error that is in the problem.

a)

b)

c)

d)

GO-12.   Robert and Diondra were working with fraction circles and were asked to represent
          thirds in two different ways. Their drawings are below. Tanisha said, "One of the
          pictures is incorrect." Which picture is incorrect, and why?

          Note: The icon below the problem number at left indicates that the authors have
          included one or more errors in the problem for you to identify and correct.

GO-13.

```
╔══════════════════════════════════════════════════════════════════╗
║                     COMMON MEASUREMENTS                            ║
║                                                                    ║
║        Length            Volume (fluid)              Weight        ║
║   12 inches = 1 foot    8 ounces = 1 cup      16 ounces = 1 pound  ║
║   36 inches = 1 yard    16 ounces = 1 pint    2,000 pounds = 1 ton ║
║     3 feet = 1 yard      2 pints = 1 quart                         ║
║  5, 280 feet = 1 mile    4 quarts = 1 gallon                       ║
║                                                                    ║
║              Temperature                        Time               ║
║      Fahrenheit          Celsius         60 seconds = 1 minute     ║
║                                          60 minutes = 1 hour       ║
║      212°   Water Boils      100°        24 hours  = 1 day         ║
║      98.6°  Body Temperature 37°          7 days  = 1 week         ║
║      72°    Room Temperature 22°        365 days = 1 year          ║
║      32°    Water Freezes    0°          52 weeks = 1 year         ║
║                                                                    ║
║                  Centuries                                         ║
║            1800's = 19th century                                   ║
║            1900's = 20th century                                   ║
║            2000's = 21st century                                   ║
╚══════════════════════════════════════════════════════════════════╝
```

In your Tool Kit, highlight the measurement facts that you do not know from memory.

GO-14.   The Niesenbahn railway in Switzerland has many stair steps. It has 42 more steps than four Empire State Buildings!

a)   If the Empire State Building has 2908 steps, how many steps are in the Niesenbahn Railway?

b)   Each step in both buildings rises six inches. How many feet of climbing occurs in each building?

GO-15.   The **range** of a set of data is the difference between the largest value and the smallest value.

a)   The following scores represent the first fourteen tests that Mrs. Poppington has corrected: 62, 65, 93, 51, 55, 76, 79, 85, 55, 72, 78, 83, 91, and 82. Find the highest test score. Find the lowest test score.

b)   Find the range of the data.

c)   Explain how you determined the range. Use a complete sentence.

GO-16. Copy each problem, then compute the sum or difference.

a)   4.3 + 2.6   b)   9.7 + 6.5   c)   1.8 + 0.3

d)   7.6 – 5.8   e)   4.3 – 2.7   f)   9.2 – 8.8

GO-17. **Solving a Problem Using Guess and Check**

Dr. Tasha McNeil, the local orthodontist, saw eight
more patients on Tuesday than on Monday. Dr.
McNeil knew that the total number of patients for the
two days was 44 because she had a stack of 44 folders.
Each patient has exactly one folder. How many folders
should be stacked in the Monday pile?

Sometimes the easiest way to get started is to guess
what the answer might be and then to check to see if
you are right. Guessing is a good strategy for learning
more about the problem, and it will lead to algebraic solutions later in the course. The
example below leads you through the four steps of a Guess and Check table. Follow along
with your teacher and help Dr. McNeil find out how many folders are in the Monday pile.

Step 1:   Set up a table. The first column will contain your guess. In this case, you will
          be guessing the number of folders for Monday. Copy the table as shown
          below on your paper.

Guess Number of Folders for Monday	

Step 2:   Make a guess about the number of folders for Monday. Your first guess
          should be something reasonable and easy. Since you know the total number
          of folders is 44, it would be silly to guess anything bigger. Try guessing 10.
          Place your guess of 10 in the box under the heading "Guess Number of
          Folders for Monday."

Guess Number of Folders for Monday	
10	

Step 3:   If there were ten folders on Monday, how many folders will be in the Tuesday
          stack? Label the top row as shown, then write that number in the space below.

Guess Number of Folders for Monday	Number of Folders for Tuesday	
10		

Step 4:   Your first guess of 10 folders for Monday means there must be 18 folders for
          Tuesday. You can use this information to determine your next column. Label
          the column "Total Number of Folders" and write the total in the space below.

Guess Number of Folders for Monday	Number of Folders for Tuesday	Total Number of Folders	
10	18	28	

>>Problem continues on the next page.>>

Step 5: Next you check to see whether your guess gives you the correct result. The last column should be checking if the total number of folders is equal to 44. If it is not, write in "too high" or "too low." Add this information to your paper.

Guess Number of Folders for Monday	Number of Folders for Tuesday	Total Number of Folders	Check 44
10	18	28	too low

Step 6: Start over with a new guess. Since the last guess was too low, we need to guess something higher. Try guessing 20, then repeat steps three through five.

Guess Number of Folders for Monday	Number of Folders for Tuesday	Total Number of Folders	Check 44
10	18	28	too low
20	28	48	too high

Step 7: Twenty folders for Monday turned out to be too high. Now you know the solution is something less than 20 but greater than 10. Try guessing 15 and repeat the process.

Guess Number of Folders for Monday	Number of Folders for Tuesday	Total Number of Folders	Check 44
10	18	28	too low
20	28	48	too high
15	23	38	too low

Step 8: Fifteen is too low. Try guessing 18 folders.

Guess Number of Folders for Monday	Number of Folders for Tuesday	Total Number of Folders	Check 44
10	18	28	too low
20	28	48	too high
15	23	38	too low
18	26	44	correct

Step 9: You have now solved the problem. There is only one thing left to do: write the answer in a complete sentence that restates the question.

Eighteen folders should be stacked in the Monday pile.

GO-18. Using the Guess and Check table below, find two consecutive numbers that have a sum of 37. (**Consecutive** means "one after another in order," like 3 and 4.) Answer in a complete sentence.

Guess First Number	Second Number	Total of Both Numbers (Sum)	Check 37
10	(10) + 1 = 11	(10) + (11) = 21	too low

GO-19.   Parts (a) and (b) below help you solve the following problem using a Guess and Check table.

The length of a rectangle is three centimeters greater than the width. If the perimeter (distance around) equals 54 centimeters, find the dimensions (length and width) of the rectangle.

a)   In this case, a diagram would be useful. Copy the diagram at right on your paper.

b)   Copy and complete the table below. Remember to show all of your calculations and to answer using a complete sentence.

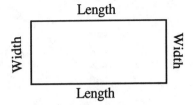

Guess Width	Length of Rectangle	Perimeter of Rectangle	Check 54
10	(10) + 3 = 13	(10) + (13) + (10) + (13) = 46	too low

GO-20.

```
┌──────────────────────────────────────────────────────────┐
│                  STUDY TEAM GUIDELINES                     │
│                                                            │
│   1.  Each member of the team is responsible for his or    │
│       her own behavior.                                    │
│                                                            │
│   2.  Each member of the team must be willing to help      │
│       any other team member who asks for help.             │
│                                                            │
└──────────────────────────────────────────────────────────┘
```

Highlight the words "each member" and "willing to help" in your Tool Kit.

GO-21.

Saul and Paul had to draw a line graph to show the temperature at different times of the day. Their data are in the table below right. When they compared their graphs, they were surprised to see that they were different.

a)   Whose graph is correct?

b)   Explain what is wrong with the other graph.

Note: The symbol on the base of the axis for temperature is an acceptable way to show that the graph does not begin at 0.

Time	Temperature
8:00 a.m.	68°
10:00 a.m.	76°
11:00 a.m.	78°
1:00 p.m.	85°
2:00 p.m.	87°

>>Problem continues on the next page.>>

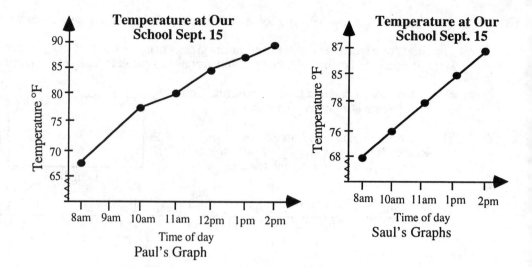

Paul's Graph

Saul's Graphs

GO-22.

INTERVALS, SCALING AND THE NUMBER LINE

The numbers on the axes of a graph show the **SCALING** of the axes. The difference between consecutive markings tells the size of the **INTERVAL**. When you scale each axis you must use <u>equal</u> intervals to represent the data accurately. For example, an interval of 5 creates a scale numbered 0, 5, 10, 15, etc. Unequal intervals distort the relationship in the data.

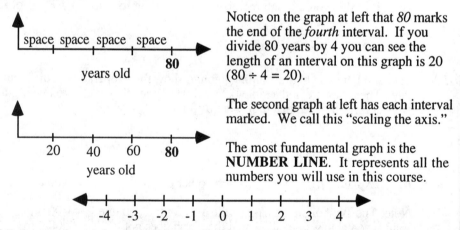

Notice on the graph at left that *80* marks the end of the *fourth* interval. If you divide 80 years by 4 you can see the length of an interval on this graph is 20 ($80 \div 4 = 20$).

The second graph at left has each interval marked. We call this "scaling the axis."

The most fundamental graph is the **NUMBER LINE**. It represents all the numbers you will use in this course.

While integer intervals are shown, fractions, π, square roots, and other numbers can be placed in the corresponding intervals.

Write the following information to the right of the double-lined box in your Tool Kit.

a) Intervals (spacing) on an axis must be the same size.

b) For scaling, the difference between consecutive numbers must be the same.

GO-23.   Copy the incomplete axes and fill in the missing numbers on the graphs.

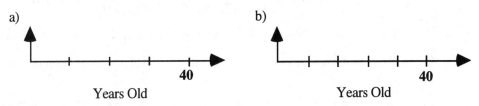

a)   b)

              40   **40**

        Years Old   Years Old

GO-24.   Mrs. Poppington is correcting math tests. Here are the scores for the first fourteen tests
          she has corrected: 62, 65, 93, 51, 55, 12, 79, 85, 55, 72, 78, 83, 91 and 76. Which
          score does not seem to fit in this set of data? Explain.

GO-25.   Kris said, "The Rawlings Rockets basketball team does
          not have any really tall players. These are their heights in
          inches: 70, 77, 75, 68, 88, 70, and 72."

          a)   Which number does not seem to fit this set of data?

          b)   Do you agree or disagree with Kris? Explain.

GO-26.   Sometimes a few pieces of a data set are significantly outside the range of most of the data.
          These data are called **outliers**. Identify the outlier(s) in the following two data sets.

          a)   5, 9, 4, 6, 9, 35, 4, 7, 10   b)   84, 79, 72, 9, 80, 84, 70

          c)   Explain why you chose these numbers.

GO-27.   Follow your teacher's directions for practicing mental math. There are several ways to do
          the problem. Which method do you think was best?

GO-28.   Follow your teacher's directions and play Logic Games with your team.

GO-29.

==

STUDY TEAM GUIDELINES

1. Each member of the team is responsible for his or her own behavior.

2. Each member of the team must be willing to help any other team member who asks for help.

3. **When you have a question, ask your partner or team first. If no one can answer the question, then ask the teacher for help.**

==

Make these notes in your Tool Kit to the right of the double-lined box for study team guidelines.

a)   Why do you think this is a study team guideline?

b)   Write an example of a question a member of the team would be able to answer.

c)   Write an example of a question that your teacher would need to answer.

GO-30.

==

MEAN, OUTLIERS, and RANGE

The **MEAN** is the arithmetic average of a data set. One way to determine the mean is to add all values in a set of data and divide the sum by the number of values.

Example: Find the mean of this set of data: 38, 42, 50, 40, and 35.
• 38 + 42 + 50 + 40 + 35 = 205
• 205 ÷ 5 (the number of values) = 41, so the mean is 41.

OUTLIERS are numbers in a data set that are either much higher or much lower than the other numbers in the set.

Example: Find the outlier of this set of data: 88, 90, 96, 93, 87, 12, 85, and 94. The outlier is 12.

The **RANGE** of a set of data is the difference between the maximum (highest value) and minimum (lowest value).

Example: Find the range of this set of data: 114, 109, 131, 96, 140, and 128.
• The highest value is 140.
• The lowest value is 96.
• 140 – 96 = 44, so the range is 44.

The mean is generally the best measure of central tendency to use when the set of data does not contain outliers.

==

Make these notes in your Tool Kit to the right of the double-lined box.

a)   List three kinds of data for which you might need to find the mean.

b)   Create an example of a set of data that contains an outlier.

c)   State the range of the data set you created in part (b).

GO-31.   Use the following data set to answer the questions below.

         62, 65, 93, 51, 55, 12, 79, 85, 55, 72, 78, 83, 91, 76

a)   Find the mean of all the scores.

b)   Now find the mean without the outlier.

c)   What did including the outlier do to the mean?

d)   Find the range of the data and explain how you found it.

GO-32.   Use the following data set to answer the questions below.

         70, 77, 75, 68, 88, 70, 72

a)   Find the mean of all the heights.

b)   Now find the mean without the outlier.

c)   What did including the outlier do to the mean?

GO-33.

SOLVING PROBLEMS WITH GUESS AND CHECK TABLES

- Read the problem carefully. Make notes or sketch a picture to organize the information in the problem.
- Look at the question being asked. Decide what you are going to guess. Set up a table. Leave extra space for more columns in case you need them.
- Calculate the entry for a column and label the column.
- Continue the table until the check is correct.
- Write the answer in a complete sentence.

Example: The sum of two consecutive numbers is 29. What are the numbers?

Guess First Number	Second Number	Total of Numbers (Sum)	Check 29
10	$(10) + 1 = 11$	$(10) + (11) = 21$	too low
20	$(20) + 1 = 21$	$(20) + (21) = 41$	too high
15	$(15) + 1 = 16$	$(15) + (16) = 31$	too high
14	$(14) + 1 = 15$	$(14) + (15) = 29$	correct

The sum of the two consecutive numbers 14 and 15 is 29.

Answer the questions below in your Tool Kit to the right of the double-lined box.

a)   What is the easiest part of using Guess and Check tables?

b)   What is the hardest part of using Guess and Check tables?

GO-34. Erin and Jacob decided to play a game in which Erin thinks of a number and Jacob tries to guess it. Erin says, "My number is the first of three consecutive numbers whose sum is 132." Use the following Guess and Check table and help Jacob figure out the number. Remember to answer using a complete sentence. Reminder: consecutive numbers are integers that follow one another in order, like 6, 7, and 8.

Guess First Number	Second Number	Third Number	Total of Numbers (Sum)	Check 132
10	(10) + 1 = 11	(10) + 2 = 12	(10) + (11) + (12) = 33	too low

GO-35. Casey and Karissa's father has asked them to construct a rectangular pen for their very athletic pig. They have 74 feet of fencing. Because the pig likes to run, they want the length to be one foot more than double the width. Use a Guess and Check table to help Karissa and Casey find the dimensions (both length and width) of the pen.

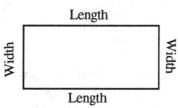

Copy and complete the table below.

Guess Width of Pen	Double the Width	Length of Pen	Perimeter	Check 74
10	2 · (10) = 20	(20) + 1 = 21	(10) + (21) + (10) + (21) = 62	too low

GO-36. Zamala made the graph shown below right and thought it looked a little unusual.

Person	Jump Height
Bev	11 inches
Jon	19 inches
Merci	6 inches
Howie	10 inches
Zamala	18 inches

Jump Heights of 5 students

a) Write a note to Zamala and tell him what he could do to improve his graph.

b) Redraw his graph using your suggested changes.

GO-37.   Copy these incomplete axes. Use your Tool Kit entry from problem GO-22 to find the missing numbers on each graph.

a)   b)   c)   d)

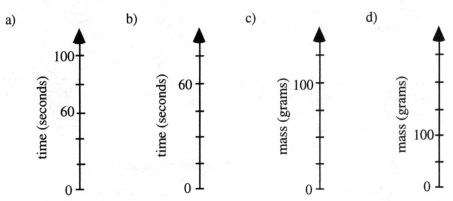

GO-38.   The longest movie ever made was called *The Longest and Most Meaningless Movie in the World*. If you sat through the entire movie, you would sit for exactly 2880 minutes.

a)   How many hours is 2880 minutes?

b)   How many days is 2880 minutes?

GO-39.   Draw a picture to represent each percent.

a)   25%   b)   75%   c) $33\frac{1}{3}\%$

GO-40.   Follow your teacher's directions for practicing mental math. Explain which solution method you liked best.

GO-41.   The **median** of a set of data is the value that is in the middle of the data set. Mrs. Poppington has just recorded these test scores in her grade book: 62, 65, 93, 51, 55, 76, 79, 85, 55, 72, 78, 83, 91, and 82.

a)   Put the test scores in order from smallest to largest.

b)   Find the median of the test scores.

c)   Explain how you determined the median. Use a complete sentence.

d)   What is the **mode** (the value that occurs most often) of the test scores?

GO-42.   Edwin and Saul collected some data   **Test Score Data**
about test scores from a recent
spelling test. They decided that a
stem-and-leaf plot would be the
best way to display their data.

The stem-and-leaf plot at right
shows the test score data. With your
partner, examine this stem-and-leaf
plot and record your answers to the
following questions.

a)   What is the highest score? What is the lowest score?

b)   What is the mode?

c)   How many scores are there? Write each score.

d)   What is the mean of the scores?

e)   What is the median score?

f)   What part of the score becomes the "stem"?

g)   How are the "stem" parts organized?

h)   How are the "leaf" parts organized?

i)   Why do you think this graph is called a "stem-and-leaf plot"? Be sure to answer in a complete sentence.

j)   Rotate the stem-and-leaf plot 90° counter-clockwise (that is, to the left). What kind of graph does the stem-and-leaf plot look like now?

GO-43.   Follow your teacher's directions for Pencils in the
Middle before starting this problem.

Edwin and Saul asked some of their classmates in
third-period math class to write down the number
of minutes they spend on the phone each day.
Here is the data set they collected: 25, 30, 88, 12,
15, 35, 20, 5, 17, 65, 16, 12, 20, 60, 75, 93, 75,
55, 50, 45, 40, 80.

a)   Display Edwin and Saul's data on a stem-and-leaf plot.

b)   What is the greatest number of minutes spent on the phone? What is the least?

c)   Is there an even or odd number of entries? Explain how you will compute the median. What is the median?

>>Problem continues on the next page.>>

d) Find the mode (that is, find the number that occurs most often). Is there more than one number that occurs most often? If there are two modes, the data is **bimodal**. If there are three modes, the data is **trimodal**. How would you describe the mode of Edwin and Saul's data?

e) Edwin and Saul are having a disagreement about the mean. Edwin says that he added up all the minutes and the mean is 933 minutes. Saul thinks the mean is approximately 42 minutes. Who is correct? Explain why.

f) Find the mean. (The minutes really do add to 933.)

g) What are you able to see on a stem-and-leaf plot that you cannot see on a bar graph?

GO-44.

Make these notes in your Tool Kit to the right of the double-lined box.

Rewrite the fourth guideline in your own words.

GO-45.

╔══╗
║   **STEM-AND-LEAF PLOT**   ║

A **STEM-AND-LEAF PLOT** is a way to display data that shows the individual values from a set of data and how the values are distributed. The "stem" part of the graph represents the leading digit of the number. The "leaf" part of the graph represents the other digit(s) of the number.

Example: Students in a math class received the following scores on their test: 49, 52, 54, 58, 61, 61, 67, 68, 72, 73, 73, 73, 78, 82, and 83. Display the test score data on a stem-and-leaf plot.

```
4 | 9                "leaf"
5 | 2 4 8                          ┌─────────────────────────────┐
6 | 1 1 7 8                        │ Key                         │
7 | 2 3 3 3 8                      │ 8| 2 3    means "82"         │
8 | 2 3                            │           and "83"          │
                                   └─────────────────────────────┘
  "stem"
```
╚══╝

Highlight the words "stem," "represents the leading digit," "leaf," and "represents the other digit(s)" in your Tool Kit.

GO-46. Display this set of data on a stem-and-leaf plot: 4.7, 3.2, 5.3, 7.2, 5.1, 7, 4.1, 3.7, 2.8, 4.3, 5.8, 6.2, 7.7, 1.5. Read all three parts below before you start your stem-and-leaf plo[t]

    a) What is different about this set of data?

    b) What digits will form the "stem"?

    c) What digits make the "leaf"?

GO-47. One number is 17 less than another and the sum of the two numbers is 65. What are the numbers? Make a Guess and Check table and continue guessing until you find the correct answer. Remember that you must make at least four meaningful guesses. Write your answer in a complete sentence.

Guess First Number	Second Number	Sum of Two Numbers	Check 65
20	20 – 17 = 3	20 + 3 = 23	too low

GO-48. Copy each problem, then compute the sum or difference. Remember to show all your steps.

    a) 23.6 + 12   b) 16.5 + 52.43   c) 46.21 – 31.2

    d) 27.5 – 13.11   e) 94.3 – 22.6   f) 109.08 – 73.8

GO-49. Copy these incomplete axes and add their scales. You may use your Tool Kit to help find missing numbers.

GO-50. Tanisha drew a picture to represent one-half. Natasha drew a picture to represent one-fourth. Wyman looked at the drawings and said, "Your pictures are wrong. One-half is supposed to be bigger than one-fourth." Do you agree with Wyman? Explain why or why not.

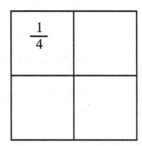

GO-51. Margaret had almost finished her homework and was finding the median of a set of numbers. She knew that there were five numbers and that the median was 21.

a) Four of the numbers were 1, 23, 16, and 100. What could the other number have been?

b) Suppose four of the numbers were 1, 21, 16, and 100. What could the other number have been?

GO-52. When you see the icon at left under a problem number, expect the problem to be challenging.

A palindrome reads the same forward as backward. Palindromes can be words ("ewe"), phrases ("a Toyota"), sentences ("Able was I ere I saw Elba"—about Napoleon), numbers (27,572), or times (6:36). This problem is about time as displayed on a digital watch.

a) Write down three digital watch times that are palindromes.

b) What are the least and greatest amounts of time between two times that are palindromes?

c) How many times during a 24-hour day is the time on a digital watch a palindrome?

GO-53. Follow your teacher's directions to list characteristics you and your partner or team have in common and characteristics that are unique to each of you.

GO-54.   Here are Mrs. Poppington's class test scores arranged in order from smallest to largest: 51, 55, 55, 62, 65, 72, 76, 78, 79, 82, 83, 85, 91, and 93.

   a)   Copy the list of scores on your paper.

   b)   Circle the median number.

   c)   Find the median of the <u>lower half</u> of your data, that is, the numbers to the left of the median. Draw a box around it. This number marks the **lower quartile** of the data set.

   d)   Find the median of the <u>upper half</u> of your data, that is, the numbers to the right of the median. Draw a box around it. This number marks the **upper quartile** of the data set.

GO-55.   Find the numbers that define the median and quartiles for the following sets of numbers.

   a)   10, 11, 12, 12, 12, 15, 17, 20, 21, 22, 30, 35, 35

   b)   10, 11, 12, 12, 12, 15, 17, 20, 21, 22, 30, 40, 50, 66

   c)   17, 11, 100, 35, 46

GO-56.   Another way of displaying data is called a **box-and-whisker plot**. Start with a number line. The box-and-whisker plot is drawn above it. A box-and-whisker plot requires data to be ordered from smallest to largest.
You also need to know the range. We will use the data from problem GO-54 to draw a box-and-whisker plot. An outline of a box-and-whisker plot is shown at right to help you draw the one for this data.

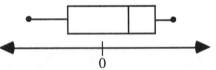

   a)   Since the range of the numbers is 42 (93 to 51), draw a number line with equal intervals, each interval representing five units, from 50 to 95.

   b)   Draw a vertical line segment (about two centimeters long) above the median. Write the number it represents below it.

   c)   Place a vertical line segment above the median of the lower half of the data. Write the number it represents below it.

   d)   Place a vertical line segment above the median of the upper half of the data. Write the number it represents below it.

   e)   Draw a box between the upper quartile and the lower quartile, using the line segments you drew above each quartile as the vertical sides.

   f)   Place two dots above the number line, one that labels the minimum (the smallest number) and another that labels the maximum (the largest number) values of the data set.

   g)   Draw a line segment from the lower quartile to the minimum value's dot and a line segment from the upper quartile to the maximum value's dot. The line segments extending to the far right and left of the data display are called the **whiskers**.

GO-57.   Edwin and Saul decided to collect more data from the second-period math class. They got permission from the second-period math teacher and asked 22 other students to write down the number of minutes they spent on the phone. Here are their results: 45, 37, 25, 20, 15, 13, 60, 65, 12, 8, 8, 75, 90, 100, 120, 15, 10, 20, 35, 42, 50, 35.

     a)   Display Edwin and Saul's new data on a new stem-and-leaf plot.

     b)   Now display the same data on a box-and-whisker plot.

GO-58.   Gracie loves to talk on the phone, but her parents try to restrict her calls. They kept records of the time she spent on the phone each day. For the past nine days the data was: 120, 60, 0, 30, 15, 0, 0, 10, and 20.

     a)   Find the mean, median, and mode for the information.

     b)   Which of the three measures in part (a) might give Gracie's parents the most accurate information about her phone use?

GO-59.   Marvin and Troy were talking about circles. Marvin said that the line that goes from one side of the circle to the other and passes through the center is the radius. Troy disagreed and said that line is the circumference. Help Marvin and Troy by drawing the circle and labeling the circumference, diameter, and radius.

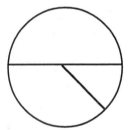

GO-60. Casey and Karissa decided to play a joke on their father and rearranged the pig pen in the shape of a triangle. They used all 74 feet of fencing to make the triangular pen. The second side of the triangle was twice the length of the first, and the third side was ten feet longer than the first. Use a Guess and Check table to find the dimensions (all three sides) of the pen.

a) Sketch a picture on your paper as shown below right.

b) Copy and complete the table. Remember to show all of your calculations and answer using a complete sentence.

Side 1   Side 2

Side 3

Guess First Side	Second Side	Third Side	Perimeter	Check 74
10	$2 \cdot (10) = 20$	$(10) + 10 = 20$	$(10) + (20) + (20) = 50$	too low

GO-61. The length of a rectangle is five more than double the width, and the perimeter is 46 yards.

a) Sketch a picture of this situation.

b) Copy and complete the Guess and Check table, making at least four guesses to find the dimensions of the rectangle.

Guess Width	Length	Perimeter	Check 46
10	$2(10) + 5 = 25$	$(10) + (25) + (10) + (25) = 70$	too high

GO-62. Copy each problem, then compute the answer. Be sure to show all your steps.

a) $7.1 \cdot 2.5$ b) $31.2 \cdot 6$ c) $12.5 \cdot 0.02$

d) Write your answer for part (c) as a percent.

GO-63.   **Diamond Problems** With your study team, see if you can discover a pattern for the numbers in each of the three diamonds below.

Finding patterns is an important problem solving skill used in mathematics. You will use the patterns in Diamond Problems to solve other problems later in the course.

Copy the Diamond Problems below and use the pattern you discovered to complete each of them.

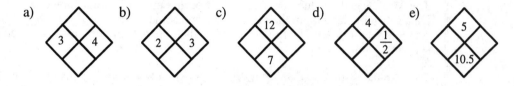

GO-64.

MEASURES OF CENTRAL TENDENCY

Numbers that locate or approximate the "center" of a set of data are called **MEASURES OF CENTRAL TENDENCY.** The mean, median, and mode are three measures of central tendency.

The **MEAN** is the arithmetic average of the data set. (See problem GO-30.) The mean is generally the best measure of central tendency to use when the set of data does not contain outliers.

The **MEDIAN** is the middle number in a set of data <u>arranged</u> <u>numerically</u>. If there is an even number of values, the median is the mean of the two middle numbers. The median is more accurate than the mean as a measure of central tendency when there are outliers in the data set.

The **MODE** is the value in a data set that occurs more often than any other value. Data sets may have more than one mode, and some do not have any mode. (See problem GO-43(d).) The mode is useful when the data are not numeric, such as showing a "most popular" choice.

Suppose the following data set represents the number of home runs hit by the best seven players on a major league baseball team: 16, 46, 21, 9, 13, 15, and 9.

The mean is $\dfrac{16 + 46 + 21 + 9 + 13 + 15 + 9}{7} = \dfrac{129}{7} \approx 18.43$.

The median is 15, since, when arranged in order—9, 9, 13, 15, 16, 21, 46—the middle number is 15.

The mode is 9, since it occurs twice and no other number appears more than once.

Highlight the words "average" (see mean), "middle number" (see median), and "occurs most often" (see mode) in your Tool Kit.

QUARTILES AND BOX-AND-WHISKER PLOTS

To find **QUARTILES**, the data set must be in order from smallest to largest. First find the median of the entire data set. Next find the median of the lower half of the data set. Finally, find the median of the upper half of the data set. The quartiles are the medians of the upper and lower halves of the data set.

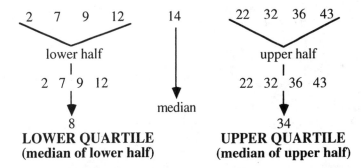

A **BOX-AND-WHISKER PLOT** displays data using quartiles. The plot and its parts appear below using the data above as a model. Problem GO-56 has the step-by-step directions for how to create a box and whisker plot.

Make these notes in your Tool Kit to the right of the double-lined box.

a) List a similarity between box-and-whisker plots and stem-and-leaf plots.

b) List a difference between box-and-whisker plots and stem-and-leaf plots.

GRAPHING POINTS ON AN XY-COORDINATE GRID

Numerical data that you want to put on a
two dimensional graph is entered on the
graph as **POINTS**.

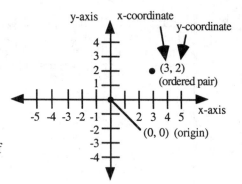

The points on the graph are identified by
two numbers, which together make an
ORDERED PAIR written generally as
(x, y). For example, (3, 2). These two
numbers are called **COORDINATES**
because together they name the location of
the point on the graph.

The first number of the ordered pair is the
X-COORDINATE because it represents the horizontal distance from (0, 0).

The second number of the ordered pair is the **Y-COORDINATE** because it
represents the vertical distance from (0, 0).

The ordered pair (3, 2) is located at a point that is right 3 units and up 2 units from
the **ORIGIN**, (0, 0). The scaled lines are called the **X-AXIS** (horizontal) and
Y-AXIS (vertical).

Make these notes in your Tool Kit to the right of the double-lined box.

a) In your own words, explain what an ordered pair means.

b) Explain how you would place the ordered pair (-4, 3) on a graph. Mark it on the
graph in your Tool Kit and check with your partner or team when you return to class
to be sure you did so correctly.

c) Review the earlier Tool Kit entry that describes a complete graph.

GO-67. Copy each problem, then compute the answer. Show all your steps.

a) $62.9 \cdot 0.7$ b) $53.2 \cdot 0.34$ c) $68.24 \cdot 7.32$

GO-68. Erin and Jacob decided to play one more round of the "guess the number" game. Erin
thought the last number she gave Jacob was too easy, so this time she said, "I'm thinking
of two consecutive even numbers whose product is 528." Jacob said, "I see how you're
trying to trick me, but it won't work." Use a Guess and Check table to help Jacob find
the numbers. Copy and complete the table. Remember to answer using a complete
sentence.

Guess First Number	Second Number	Product	Check 528
10	(10) + 2 = 12	(10) · (12) = 120	too low

GO-69.   Mrs. Poppington has finally finished grading her tests. The first set of scores was: 62, 65, 93, 51, 55, 76, 79, 85, 55, 72, 78, 83, 91, and 82. The last scores are: 88, 74, 97, 32, 82, 76, 59, 63, 89, and 77. Complete parts (a) through (e) for all the scores.

a)   Find the median.   b)   Find the range.

c)   Find the mode.   d)   Find the quartiles.

e)   Find the mean.   f)   Draw a box-and-whisker plot for the data.

GO-70.   Follow your teacher's directions for practicing mental math. What new solution method did you learn today?

GO-71.   Dezzirae's oldest brother Kalani has saved enough money to buy a car. Kalani told Dezzirae, "Buying a car will actually be a good investment. I can buy it now and sell it when I need the money back. Except for buying gas, it will be almost free because I can get all my money back when I sell it."

Dezzirae exclaimed, "Kalani, I think you should collect some information before you make that kind of statement. Investing your money in a car is not a good idea!"

"I don't agree with you, Dezzirae!" Kalani replied. Collect, organize, and analyze some data to help Dezzirae and Kalani settle their disagreement.

a)   Your team needs to collect data on the prices of used cars. You can find this information in the want ads of the newspaper. Your teacher may have some other ideas about where you can find this information. Select one manufacturer of cars and one model. Try to pick a model of car that has been produced for a few years. Split the work among your team so that you can collect the data as quickly as possible. One member of the team should use a table like the one below to record the data for the team. You will want to have at least 15 entries in your table. Once you have collected the data, each team member needs to copy the data table.

Manufacturer of Car _____ Model of Car _____

Price of Car	Year of Car	Age of Car

b)   What is the range in the prices of your data? What is the range in the ages of the cars? Use this information to scale the axes on the graph you will create in part (c).

>>Problem continues on the next page.>>

c)   Enter the data on the graph. Do not connect the points. This is called a **scatter plot.** Use the example at right to help you set up your graph. Using graph paper may make it easier for you to plot the data.

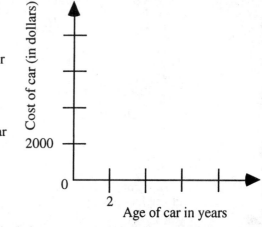

d)   Examine the points on your scatter plot. Does there appear to be a relationship between the age of the car and the cost of the car? Using complete sentences, describe what you see.

e)   Based on your scatter plot, what information would you give Dezzirae and Kalani to help them settle their argument? Can Kalani get all his money back if he sells his car in a couple of years? Explain why it would have been beneficial for Dezzirae and Kalani to collect and graph some data before getting into an argument.

GO-72.   Your teacher will give you a resource page for this problem.

a)   On the resource page, plot the following points in a bright color and draw a line through them: (2, 40), (3, 40), (4, 40), (5, 40), (6, 40), and $(3\frac{1}{2}, 40)$.

b)   What do you notice? Write your answer in a complete sentence.

c)   Write the ordered pairs for two other points that would be on the same line as the points in part (a).

GO-73.   Use the resource page provided by your teacher.

a)   On the resource page, plot the following points in a bright color and draw a line through them: (550, 72), (550, 66), (550, 69), and (550, 79).

b)   What do you notice? Write your answer in a complete sentence.

c)   Write the ordered pairs for two other points which would be on the same line.

GO-74.   Use the resource page provided by your teacher.

a)   Label each axis.

b)   Plot the following ordered pairs (points) and draw a line through them:
(-4, -4), (-2, -3), (0, -2), (2, -1), (4, 0), (6, 1).

c)   What do you notice? Write the ordered pairs for two other points that would be on the same line.

GO-75.   Use the resource page provided by your teacher.

    a)   Label each axis. Plot the following ordered pairs: (2, 3), (-2, 3), (-2, -3), (2, -3). Connect the points <u>as</u> <u>you</u> <u>plot</u> <u>them</u>.

    b)   Describe the shape on your graph.

    c)   Plot a triangle on the same set of axes. List the ordered pairs needed for your triangle.

GO-76.   Karissa and Casey need to construct another pig pen for their grand champion pig named Beauty. Large pigs like Beauty need at least 108 square feet of living space. Karissa and Casey made the length 3 feet longer than the width and created exactly 108 square feet of area for Beauty. Use a Guess and Check table to find the dimensions (length and width) of the pen.

    a)   Sketch a picture on your paper like the one shown at right.

    b)   Copy and complete the table below. Remember to answer using a complete sentence.

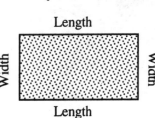

Guess Width	Length	
10	(10) + 3 = 13	

GO-77.   Copy and complete the Diamond Problems below. Notice the icon under the problem number at left. Use the diamond problem pattern to solve these problems.

Product

Sum

a)   b)   c)   d)   e)

GO-78.   Organized binders do not have loose papers in them.
The "Shake Test" is a technique you can use to see if
your papers are locked into your binder. Hold your
binder along the spine and <u>gently</u> shake it. If any papers
fall out, they will need to be placed back in the binder in
the correct location. You may need to purchase hole
reinforcement stickers, hole-punch some papers, or
simply place papers in their correct place. Work on
your binder until it passes the "Shake Test." When
this is completed, write "My binder has passed the
shake test" next to this problem number on your paper.
Your teacher may actually try the "Shake Test" on your
binder tomorrow.

GO-79.

Chapter Summary As you finish a chapter, you need to reflect on
the material. Your teacher is going to model one way to do that. You
and your partner or team will then need to do a chapter summary of
your own.

a)   You will construct a concept map today for each chapter
objective. Your teacher will model a topic for you.

b)   Look back through your work and select two problems that
illustrate what you have learned about organizing, displaying,
and interpreting data. Restate the problem and show its
complete solution.

c)   Select a problem that you solved using a Guess and Check
table. Write the problem and show the complete solution.

GO-80.   Shelly and Melissa spent Saturday morning making
chocolate chip cookies. They counted the cookies
and discovered they had made 53 of them. Then
Shelly decided to divide the cookies. Since Shelly
was five years older than Melissa, it seemed natural
for her to get five more cookies. Draw and label a
Guess and Check table and use it to find out how
many cookies were in each sister's pile. Be sure to
show all four steps clearly.

GO-81.   Scaling the axes to plot this set of points requires some planning: (600, 5), (750, 10),
(400, 3), and (300, 0).

a)   Decide the maximum and minimum values for both the x-axis and the y-axis on
your graph.

b)   Decide what intervals to use on each axis.

c)   Draw and scale the axes so you can graph all the points.

d)   Plot the points on your graph.

GO-82.   You have a set of six numbers and know that five of them are 2, 24, 16, 17, and 12.

a)   If you know that the median is 14, what could the missing number be?

b)   If you know that the quartiles are defined by the numbers 8, 14, and 17, what could the missing number be?

GO-83.   The Road Safety Committee is concerned about the number of car accidents that occur near people's homes. They want to know if it is safer to drive a long distance or a short distance. Copy the axes below, choose and label a scale with appropriate intervals, and create a scatter plot to see if there is a relationship between distance from home and the number of accidents last year.

Distance from Home	# of Accidents Last Year
2 miles	759
5 miles	680
7 miles	700
9 miles	558
12 miles	384
15 miles	135
20 miles	82

GO-84.   The Road Safety Committee is impressed with your graph and now has some questions for you.

a)   Since there were more accidents near homes, can we conclude that being near home causes more accidents than being farther from home?

b)   Is this a **positive correlation** (as distance increases, the number of accidents also increases) or a **negative correlation** (as distance increases, the number of accidents decreases)?

c)   If we see a connection between two things (like distance and accidents), does that mean one causes the other?

GO-85.   Understanding the difference between one thing being <u>correlated</u> to another and <u>causing</u> the other is important. Write TRUE if you think the item listed causes the other; write FALSE if there is a correlation but not a cause.

a)   Being in my home causes me to fall down, because I fall down about 20 times a year at home and almost never at other people's homes.

b)   Practicing basketball causes me to shoot free throws well, because I shoot better when I practice.

c)   Turning on the "Seat Belt" light on the airplane causes turbulence, because whenever the light is turned on, the flight gets bumpy.

d)   Smoking causes lung cancer, because a lot of people who smoke get lung cancer.

e)   Being tall makes you a better speller, because a lot of people under 3 feet tall cannot spell well.

GO-86.   These questions relate to dividing by 2. Some of them may not be possible. If they are not, explain in a sentence or two why not.

a)   Find all of the digits that could be used to make the three-digit number 5__1 divisible by 2.

b)   Find all of the digits that could be used to make the three-digit number 3__6 divisible by 4.

c)   If you have an even number N (divisible by 2), can the number N + 200 also be divisible by 2? Explain in a sentence or two.

d)   If you have an odd number N (<u>not</u> divisible by 2), can the number N + 200 ever be an even number? Explain in a sentence or two.

GO-87.   Follow your teacher's directions for practicing mental math. Are you beginning to find it easier to do these type of problems? Explain.

GO-88.   Since 1904 the times for men and women in the Olympic 100-meter free-style swimming race have been decreasing. Bethany wondered if the times for the two groups would ever be the same. She needs a way to display the data to help her compare the times for men and women. The tables below show the times for the Olympic 100-meter free-style swimming races from 1904 to 2000.

>>**Problem continues on the next page.**>>

Men's 100-meter Free-style

Year	Athletes	Country	Time
1904	Z. De Halmay	Hungary	62.8
1908	C. Daniels	USA	65.6
1912	D. Kahanamoku	USA	63.4
1920	D. Kahanamoku	USA	61.4
1924	J. Weissmuller	USA	59.0
1928	J. Weissmuller	USA	58.6
1932	Y. Miyazaki	Japan	58.2
1936	F. Csik	Hungary	57.6
1948	W. Ris	USA	57.3
1952	C. Scholes	USA	57.4
1956	J. Hendricks	Australia	55.4
1960	J. Devitt	Australia	55.2
1964	D. Schollander	USA	53.4
1968	M. Wenden	Australia	52.22
1972	M. Spitz	USA	51.22
1976	J. Montgomery	USA	49.99
1980	J. Woithe	E. Germany	50.40
1984	R. Gaines	USA	49.80
1988	M. Biondi	USA	48.63
1992	A. Popov	Unified Team	49.02
1996	A. Popov	Russia	48.74
2000	P. Vanden Hoogenband	Netherlands	48.30

Women's 100-meter Free-style

Year	Athlete	Country	Time
1920	E. Bleibtrey	USA	73.6
1924	E. Lackie	USA	72.4
1928	A. Osipowich	USA	71.0
1932	H. Madison	USA	66.8
1936	H. Mastenbroek	Holland	65.9
1948	G. Andersen	Denmark	66.3
1952	K. Szoke	Hungary	66.8
1956	D. Fraser	Australia	62.0
1960	D. Fraser	Australia	61.2
1964	D. Fraser	Australia	59.5
1968	J. Henne	USA	60.0
1972	S. Neilson	USA	58.59
1976	K. Ender	E. Germany	55.65
1980	B. Krause	E. Germany	54.79
1984	Hogshead	USA	55.92
1988	K. Otto	E. Germany	54.93
1992	Z. Yong	China	54.64
1996	L. Jingyi	China	54.50
2000	I. deBruijn	Netherlands	53.83

>>Problem continues on the next page.>>

a) Use the resource page to draw a double-line graph for the men's and women's Olympic data. Make sure your legend clearly identifies each line.

b) What trends do you notice? (A trend is the general direction the line is headed.)

c) Do you think the women's times will eventually equal the men's times?

d) Why do you think there were no Olympic games in 1916, 1940, and 1944?

e) Why do you think the times were recorded in hundredths of a second beginning in 1968?

f) Which changed more, the men's or women's times? Why do you think that happened?

g) Write a response that Bethany might use after your analysis of the data.

h) What do you predict will be the men's and women's times in the next Olympics (2004)? Explain your prediction.

GO-89. Draw a set of axes like the one at right. Notice that there are 8 spaces on the y-axis. Put the years on the x-axis. Be careful about the interval on the x-axis. Read the "Intervals and Scaling" entry in your Tool Kit before numbering the x-axis. Make sure your graph is complete.

High Temperature on Jan. 1 of Various Years

Year	Temperature
1991	54° F
1993	72° F
1997	35° F
1998	42° F
1999	65° F

GO-90. Tomatoes are sold 3 for $1.20 at Bull's Eye Market.

a) How much does one tomato cost?

b) How much would 18 tomatoes cost?

GO-91. Find the mean, median, and mode of this set of data: 7.2, 3.8, 9.4, 4.7, 1.6, 11.8, 3.8, 7.2, and 6.5.

GO-92. Look in the bottom of your backpack for any loose papers. If there are any, they should be taken out and put back in your binder. Caution: There may be papers from other classes. Put those away in their proper places as well. Try the "Shake Test" to see that everything is locked in your binder. On your paper, write, "My binder has passed the shake test."

GO-93.   Copy and complete the Diamond Problems below.

Product

Sum

a)

b)

c)

d)

e)

GO-94.   A triangle has three sides. The second side is one centimeter longer than twice the length of the first side, and the third side is two centimeters shorter than the second side. The perimeter of the triangle is 125 centimeters.

   a)   Sketch a picture of this situation.

   b)   Solve the problem using a complete Guess and Check process.

Guess First Side	Second Side			
10	$2(10) + 1 = 21$			

GO-95.   The product of two consecutive odd numbers is 12,099. Complete a Guess and Check table to find the numbers.

GO-96.   **What We Have Done in This Chapter**

   Below is a list of the Tool Kit entries from this chapter.

   • GO-8   Study Team Guidelines (also GO-20, 29, and 44)
   • GO-10   A Complete Graph
   • GO-13   Common Measurements
   • GO-22   Intervals, Scaling, and the Number Line
   • GO-30   Mean, Outliers, and Range
   • GO-33   Solving Problems with Guess and Check Tables
   • GO-45   Stem-and-Leaf Plot
   • GO-64   Measures of Central Tendency
   • GO-65   Quartiles and Box-and-Whisker Plots
   • GO-66   Graphing Points on an xy-Coordinate Grid

   Review all the entries and read the notes you made in your Tool Kit. Make a list of any questions, terms, or notes you do not understand. Ask your partner or study team members for help. If anything is still unclear, ask your teacher.

THE FIELD TRIP

Chapter 2

Chapter 2
The Field Trip: INTEGER OPERATIONS AND GRAPHING EQUATIONS

In this chapter you will begin working with integer operations. You will also discover patterns in relation to data tables, rules or equations, and graphs. In addition, you will learn about the shapes of different graphs. You will continue to record data and graph real-life situations, as well as practice the problem solving strategy of Guess and Check.

In this chapter you will have the opportunity to:

- discover and describe patterns in data tables.

- graph points in all four quadrants.

- develop integer operations for addition, subtraction, multiplication, and division.

- identify and graph linear and non-linear equations.

- continue to solve word problems using the Guess and Check problem solving strategy.

Read the problem below, but **do not try to solve it now**. What you learn over the next few days will enable you to solve it.

FT-0. **The Big Hike** At Big Tree Park, Raul, the park ranger, and Mia, the chief naturalist, each led a group hike. Raul's group hiked to Grizzly Peak, which has an elevation of 182 feet. Mia's group hiked to Mt. Sawtooth, which has an elevation of 324 feet. The elevation of their campsite is 120 feet below sea level. If Mia's group hikes downhill at a rate of 3 feet per minute and Raul's group hikes downhill at a rate of 2 feet per minute, which group will arrive at the campsite first?

Number Sense		
Algebra and Functions		
Mathematical Reasoning		
Measurement and Geometry		
Statistics, Data Analysis, & Probability		

Chapter 2
The Field Trip: INTEGER OPERATIONS AND GRAPHING EQUATIONS

FT-1.   Today you will play silent board games. The directions are below. As each silent board game is played, copy the table and the rule on your paper.

Silent Board Games
A game for the whole class.

Mathematical Purpose: To find and describe mathematical relationships.

Object: To complete the table and find the rule.

Materials: None.

How to Play the Game:
- Your teacher will start an xy relationship table on the board by filling in some of the x-values and a few of the y-values.
- The class will remain silent as you try to figure out the pattern that links each x-value to each y-value.
- Raise your hand when you think you can fill in one of the blanks. Your teacher will call on students to fill in an answer silently. Then return to your seat.
- Your teacher will erase an incorrect answer.

Ending the Game: The game ends when the table is complete and someone writes the rule.

FT-2.   Your teacher will give you instructions for the Whole-Class Graphing Activity. On the resource page provided by your teacher, make a sketch of each graph based on the large class graphs and describe what each one looks like. Add any notes to these sketches that will help you draw graphs correctly.

FT-3.   Use a Guess and Check table to solve the following problem.

Raul wanted to see if the deer population had been affected by an increase in the number of visitors to the park. He decided to count the number of visitors entering the park through each of the three gates. On Saturday, 50 more people came through the South Gate than the North Gate. There were two times as many people entering through the West Gate as the North Gate. If 3202 people visited the park that day, how many entered through each of the gates?

Copy and complete the Guess and Check table below to help you answer this question. Be sure to make at least 4 guesses. Write your answer to the question using a complete sentence.

Guess Number of Visitors Entering North Gate	Number of Visitors Entering South Gate			Check 3202
10	(10) + 50 = 60			

FT-4. Use the resource page provided by your teacher that shows a map of Big Tree Park. Match each location with a point on the diagram. Keep this map in your binder for future use.

Lookout Point:	150'	Grizzly Peak:	182'
Redwood Grove:	49'	Mt. Sawtooth:	324'
Campsite:	-120'	Sea Level:	0'

FT-5. Copy each problem, then compute the answer. Show all your steps.

a) $1.234 + 0.58 + 5.316$ b) $6.1 - 1.536$ c) $4.83 \cdot 0.68$

d) $18.273 - 6.039$ e) $4.8 + 6.237 + 0.1$ f) $6.23 \cdot 0.812$

FT-6. David and his parents went on vacation. One day they drove 200 miles, traveling at the same speed the entire way. If the trip took them a total of four hours, how many miles did they drive in one hour? Show your work and write an equation.

FT-7. Here are the heights in inches of hollyhocks (tall, slender flowering plants) that are growing in the park: 10, 39, 43, 45, 46, 47, 48, 48, 49, 50, and 52.

a) Find the mean.

b) Find the mode.

c) Find the range.

d) Find the median.

e) Which measure of central tendency best represents this set of data?

f) Find the quartiles.

g) Make a box-and-whisker plot.

FT-8.   Use the resource page provided by your teacher to make your set of integer tiles. Cut out the set of squares with plus signs and the set of squares with minus signs. Store them in the envelope provided for use throughout this chapter.

FT-9.   Now that we have started a new chapter, it is time for you to organize your binder.

    a)   Put the work from the last chapter in order, take it out of your binder, and store it in a separate folder.

    b)   When this is completed, write, "I have organized my binder."

FT-10.   Follow your teacher's directions for practicing mental math. What new strategy did you learn today?

FT-11.   Your teacher will give several students bundles of envelopes containing unknown amounts of money. Do not open or look inside any of the envelopes until your teacher tells you to do so.

Make a table like the one below and follow the instructions from your teacher to complete it.

Envelope Label	Amount in Each Envelope	Total Amount of Money
↓	↓	

FT-12. The first stop on your field trip to Big Tree Park is a grove of redwood trees that are all different heights. Raul, the park ranger, explained that the height difference occurred because after the first tree was planted, additional trees were planted in 5-year intervals (That is, every five years). The tree nearest you is 85 feet tall, and the next one, which is five years older, is 90 feet tall. You are curious about their age, so you decide to graph the situation and use your graph to learn more about the age of the tree.

a) Use the data table like the one below on your resource page for the 85-foot tree.

years (x)	-5	-4	-3	-2	Last Year -1	Now 0	Next Year 1	2	3	5	10	15	20
height (y)		81	82			85	86						

b) Fill in the height of the tree for each year, assuming the tree continues to grow at the same rate.

c) How does the height of the tree change as the years go by? Study your table and describe in words the pattern you see.

d) Write a word equation that relates the height of the tree to the number of years.

FT-13. How tall will the tree be:

a) in 30 years?   b) in 50 years?   c) in any future year?

FT-14. How tall was the tree:

a) 10 years ago?   b) 20 years ago?

c) How many years ago was the tree planted?

FT-15.   Follow the steps below to graph the data from the
redwood tree in problem FT-12. Start by copying the
graph at right and extend the axes to represent the past
and future, or use the graph on your resource page.

Height
of Tree

a)   Scale the horizontal (x) axis by fives. Each tick
mark represents five years. As you number to the
right of zero, you are looking at the future. As
you number to the left of zero, you are looking at
the past, so -5 means "five years ago." Scale the vertical (y) axis by tens. Each tick
mark will represent ten feet of height.

b)   Plot the points from your table. Remember to go across to the year (x) and then
move up to the height (y).

c)   Connect the points to show the tree's continuous growth.

d)   Does it make sense for this line to continue forever in both directions? Explain.

FT-16.   Use your graph from the previous problem to answer the following questions.

a)   Find the point on your graph where your line crosses the horizontal (x) axis.
What is the height of the tree at this point? Record this in your table.

b)   What does this point represent?

FT-17.   Below is the word equation from problem FT-12.

Height = 85 + (number of years)

a)   Complete a table like the one below. Show your work as modeled in the table.

Number of Years	85 + (number of years)	Height of Tree
8	85 + 8	
5	85 + 5	90
-1	85 + (-1)	
-2	85 + ( )	
-6	85 +	
-10		

b)   What happens to the height of the tree as we move into the past? Why do you think
this is so?

FT-18. Write a numerical expression that represents each statement. Part (a) is done for you.

a) Fourteen is added to a number x.
[14 + x]

b) Forty-three is subtracted from a number y.

c) A number a is multiplied by five.

d) A number x is tripled, then seven is added.

FT-19.

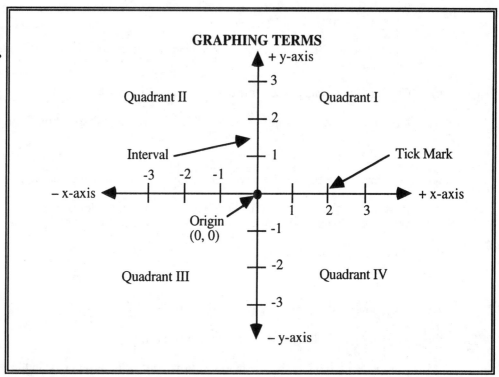

GRAPHING TERMS

Complete parts (a) through (c) below in your Tool Kit to the right of the double-lined box.

a) In your own words, describe what an interval is.

b) Tell why tick marks and a scale are needed on graphs.

c) Where on the graph is the origin?

FT-20.   Copy the graphs below. In parts (a) and (b) determine the interval used between tick
         marks. Complete the scale by labeling the remaining tick marks.

a)

         32   64

b)

                    -5   0

c)

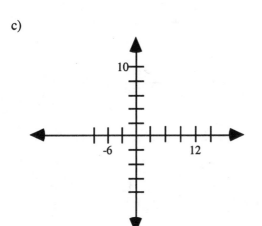

              10

         -6   12

For part (c):

i)   Label the y-axis.

ii)   Label the origin.

iii) Label Quadrant III.

iv)   Complete the scaling of both axes.

FT-21.   Mia was studying some of the pond life in the
         park. In two hours she counted 4 more frogs than
         the number of turtles she saw. The number of
         crayfish she counted was 3 more than twice the
         number of turtles. She counted 75 pond animals
         in all. Use a Guess and Check table to find the
         number of turtles, crayfish, and frogs Mia counted.

         a)   Copy and complete the table. Keep guessing
               and checking until you get the correct
               answer. Remember to make at least four
               guesses.

Guess the Number of Turtles	Number of Frogs	Number of Crayfish	Total Number of Pond Animals	Check 75
10				

         b)   Write your answer in a complete sentence.

FT-22.   Complete these Diamond Problems.

Product

Sum

a)

         5.3   8.2

b)

               2.3

         7.4

c)

              7.5

         5

d)

              14.72

         6.4

FT-23. A number n is greater than four. Which of the following graphs best represents the location of $\frac{4}{n}$ on the number line?

Note: The icon at left indicates that the problem will be in the multiple choice format.

(A)

(B)

(C)

(D)

(E)   none of the these

FT-24. What is the product of seventy-two and zero?

(A) 0   (B) 1   (C) 72   (D) -72   (E) none of these

FT-25. We changed the water in our fish tank and needed to add some acid to bring the water to the right pH. We did not have any tool to measure pH, but our neighbor had a kit for his swimming pool and told us that if our aquarium held 10,000 gallons, we would need to add 6 gallons of acid. However, our aquarium holds only six gallons of water. How many <u>teaspoons</u> of acid do we need? Note: 3 teaspoons = 1 tablespoon, 16 tablespoons = 1 cup = 8 ounces.

FT-26. As each silent board game is played, copy and complete the table, then write the equation on your paper below the table. You may want to review the rules for the game in problem FT-1.

CHAPTER 2

FT-27. Represent each integer using integer tiles two different ways. Make a sketch for each model.

a)   6   b)   -2   c)   -5   d)   0

FT-28. Use at least 12 tiles to represent each integer. Remember that you can add zero pairs to the model without changing the value of each number. Sketch a drawing for each model.

a)   5   b)   -4   c)   -7   d)   0

FT-29. Here is another example with a diagram: 5 + (-3). Use this example as your model for solving the following problems. Draw a diagram and write an equation for each problem below the example.

+ + + + +   5

+ + + + +   5 + (-3)
– – –

     + +   5 + (-3) = 2

ADDING INTEGERS

1. Build your first integer.
2. Add tiles that represent the second integer.
3. Circle all the zero pairs.
4. Count the uncircled tiles.
5. Record the equation showing the sum.

---

a)   4 + (-7)   b)   -1 + (-5)   c)   -3 + 6

FT-30. Use integer tiles to help you add the integers in each problem below. Sketch a tile drawing and write the equation for each of the following problems.

a)   -6 + (-8)   b)   2 + (-5)   c)   -3 + (-3)   d)   -2 + 3 + 5

e)   Describe the steps you used to solve part (d).

FT-31.   Copy the number line below. Remember
         to create a reasonable scale. Draw a tick
         mark and label it to show when you:

                        Now
    ◄───────────────────┼───────────────────►
                         0

    a)   lost your first tooth.

    b)   started to read.

    c)   started elementary school.

    d)   started middle school.

    e)   started high school.

FT-32.   Use the number line from the previous problem to show the following events in your life. Did
         the ages from the previous problem go before "Now" or after "Now" on the number line?

    a)   How many years ago were you born?

    b)   If "Now" is 0 and you were born sometime before now, what kind of integer should
          you use to represent when you were born? Be sure this is on your number line. It is
          important!

    c)   If "Now" is 0, in about how many years will you get your driver's license?
          Graduate from high school? Vote in your first election? Mark these ages on your
          number line and label them with the event name.

    d)   What kind of integers did you use to represent events in the future?

FT-33.   Use the table below to complete parts (a) through (c).

in (x)	0	1	2	3	4	5	6	10	100	x
out (y)	1	3				11				

    a)   Fill in the missing numbers in the table.

    b)   Use complete sentences to describe the pattern that relates input values to output
          values.

    c)   Write the equation that represents the pattern in y-form. Be sure to include the rule
          in your table.

FT-34. Use tiles to help you solve these problems. Sketch a tile drawing and write the equation below it.

a) -2 + (-3)

b) 4 + (-8)

c) -1 + (-5)

d) -7 + 4 + 2

e) Describe the steps you used to solve part (d).

FT-35. Candied apples are sold five for $2.00. Sandi wants three candied apples. How much will she have to pay for them? Show the steps you use to solve this problem.

FT-36. Irving's print shop was supposed to print the number line below. Copy the number line and write the missing numbers below each tick mark.

a) Tell Irving which is larger, 5 or 8.

b) Tell Irving which is smaller, -7 or -3.

c) Tell Irving which is smaller, -10 or 2.

d) Finally, tell Irving how he can always determine which number is larger.

FT-37. As each silent board game is played, copy and complete the table and then write the equation below the table.

FT-38. Mia explained to her study team that there are 108 wolves in the park and their number is **decreasing at a rate of three wolves per year**. She is concerned about the decline of the wolf population, so she wants your team to join her in studying the problem.

a) Copy and complete the data table or use the resource page for the wolf population from 20 years ago to help study it in the future. "Now" is represented by 0 years.

years (x)	-20	-15	Past Years -10	-5	Now 0	5	Future Years 10	15	20	x
wolves (y)				123	108	93				

b) Describe the pattern in the table using complete sentences.

c) Write an equation to represent the pattern.

d) Create a graph in which "Time in Years" is on the horizontal (x) axis. It should be scaled so that one tick mark on the graph represents ten years.

e) The vertical (y) axis will represent "Number of Wolves" and should be scaled so one tick mark represents ten wolves.

f) Plot the points from the data table.

g) Using a straightedge, draw a line to connect the points. Extend your line as far as possible on your graph.

h) The point where the line crosses the y-axis is called the **y-intercept**. What are the coordinates of this point?

i) The point where the line crosses the x-axis is called the **x-intercept**. What are the coordinates of this point?

FT-39. Use your pattern, the graph, and your table from the previous problem to answer the following questions.

a) When will the population be fewer than 50 wolves?

b) When would there have been 200 wolves?

c) In how many years will the wolves be gone from this park?

FT-40. Here is another graph for you to do more independently.

input	-3	-2	-1	0	1	2	3	x
output	-6			-3		-1		

a) Copy and complete the table above or use your resource page.

b) Make a graph of the points.

c) Draw a line to connect the points. Be sure to extend your line as far as possible on your graph.

d) Name the coordinates of the x-intercept.

e) Name the coordinates of the y-intercept.

FT-41. Copy the diagram at right into your notebook and answer the questions that follow.

-7   0   7

a) What is the distance from -7 to 0?

b) What is the distance from 7 to 0?

c) We show that the distance from -5 to 0 is 5 using absolute value notation: $|-5| = 5$. Write the absolute value notation for -7 and 7.

FT-42. Draw a number line diagram to represent the two absolute value equations below.

a) $|-4| = 4$ b) $|8| = 8$

FT-43. Copy and complete the following equations.

a) $|-17| = $ _____   b) $|42| = $ _____   c) $|3| = $ _____   d) $|-10| = $ _____

FT-44.

ABSOLUTE VALUE

ABSOLUTE VALUE is the distance a number is from zero on the number line in either direction. We use the symbol $|x|$ to indicate the absolute value of any number x. For example,

$$|-3| = 3 \text{ and } |3| = 3.$$

3 units   3 units

-4 -3 -2 -1 0 1 2 3 4

Solve for x in each part below and put your work in your Tool Kit to the right of the double-lined box.

a) $|-12| = x$ b) $|x| = 12$ c) $|x| = 8$ d) $|x| = -4$

FT-45.

COMPONENTS OF A LINEAR GRAPH

- x- and y-axes labeled and scaled
- equation (rule) written near the line
- line extended as far as possible

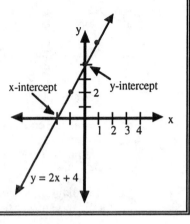

x	-1	0	1	2	3	x
y	2	4	6	8	10	$y = 2x + 4$

Make these notes in your Tool Kit to the right of the double-lined box.

a) Highlight the three bulleted items on the graph in your Tool Kit.

b) Write the coordinates of the points that represent the x- and y-intercepts.

FT 46. Examine the following table.

input	0	1	2	3	4	x
output	1	4		10		

a) Copy the table.

b) Look for a pattern between the input and output values. Complete the table.

c) Write the equation that represents the pattern.

d) Graph the equation.

e) Identify the coordinates for the x-intercept and the y-intercept.

f) Use your Tool Kit for "Components of a Linear Graph" to make sure your graph in this problem is complete.

FT-47. Copy and complete the table. Be sure to include the rule.

input	4	2	0	1		3	x
output		9		7	15		

FT-48.   Write a numerical expression that represents each statement.

     a)   A negative four is added to a number.

     b)   A number y is multiplied by six.

     c)   A number c is multiplied by seven then negative five is added.

     d)   A number x is divided by eight.

FT-49.   Use tiles to do the following computations. Sketch a tile drawing and write an equation for each one.

     a) $6 + (-3)$

     b) $5 + (-2)$

     c) $7 + (-5)$

     d) $6 + (-8)$

     e) $5 + (-9)$

     f) $7 + (-10)$

     g)   What pattern do you see when adding integers with opposite signs?

     h)   Explain how you would add $12 + (-20)$ without using integer tiles.

FT-50.

ADDITION OF INTEGERS

If the signs are the same, combine by adding the absolute value of each number and keep the same sign.

If the signs are different, ignore them. Then subtract the smaller number from the larger number and keep the sign of the original number that has the larger absolute value.

Example 1:
add $-5 + (-3)$
$|-5| = 5$ and $|-3| = 3$
$5 + 3 = 8$
Both signs are $-$, so $-5 + (-3) = -8$

Example 2:
add $-4 + 2$
$|-4| = 4$ and $|2| = 2$
$4 - 2 = 2$
4 is greater than 2, so $-4 + 2 = -2$

Put two examples of adding integers to the right of the double-lined box in your Tool Kit. One example must have at least one negative integer. When you return to class, have your partner or a teammate check that your examples are correct.

FT-51.   Compute.

     a) $-16 + 3$

     b) $10 + (-91)$

     c) $-14 + (-4)$

FT-52.   As each silent board game is played, copy and complete the table, then write the equation below the table.

FT-53.   Refer to the graph and table from problem FT-38.

a)   On your graph, the present year or "Now"
      is represented by 0. Five years from now is
      represented by 5. How was five years **ago**
      represented?

b)   How many wolves were there five years ago?
      Ten years ago?

FT-54.   Below is the equation for the number of wolves from problem FT-38.

          Number of wolves = 108 – (3 times the number of years from now)

          $$y = 108 - 3x$$

a)   Use the equation and your graph to complete the table below. A few entries are
      done for you.

Number of Years (x)	108 – 3(Number of Years)	Number of Wolves (y)
-200	108 – (-600)	708
-7	108 – (-21)	129
-5		
3	108 – (9)	99
7		
10		

b)   How did you find the number of wolves 200 years ago?

c)   What happens to the number of wolves as we move into the past?

d)   Describe what happens when you subtract a negative integer from 108.

FT-55.   To compute -9 – 4 using tiles, start with nine negative tiles.

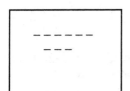

The problem, -9 – 4, requires that
we remove four positive tiles.

However, there are no positive tiles
in the box.

a)   Pairs of + and – tiles have been added to each of the following boxes. Evaluate the
number that each box of tiles represent.

i)   ii)   iii)

b)   From which box in part (a) can four positive tiles be removed? Copy this box and
remove the four positive tiles.

c)   After removing the four positive tiles, evaluate the number of tiles left in the box.
This is the answer to the problem -9 – (+4).

d)   Compute 7 – (-2) using integers tiles. Show your drawing and write an equation.

FT-56.   Use integer tiles to do the following subtraction problems. Sketch a tile drawing and
write an equation for each one.

a)   -7 – (-3)   b)   -12 – 8

c)   6 – 4   d)   5 – 8

FT-57.   An example of how to use a tile diagram to subtract integers is shown below. Use the
diagram as a model to help solve the problems that follow.

-7 – 4

-7 – 4 = -11

a)   -6 – 5   b)   -10 – 3   c)   10 – (-5)   d)   -3 – (-7)

>>Problem continues on the next page.>>

FT-58.   Use integer tiles to solve these problems. Sketch a tile drawing and write the equation below it.

a)   -9 – 2   b)   7 – (-4)   c)   -6 – (-8)

FT-59.   Use a Guess and Check table to solve the following problem.

On a day when they were studying the deer population, Raul and Mia decided to try to figure out the number of deer in the park. Raul counted twice as many as Mia. If together they counted 405 deer, how many deer did Mia count? How many did Raul count?

FT-60.   Complete the table for the equation $y = 4x – 5$, then graph the equation.

input (x)	2	3	0	1	4	x
output (y)						4x – 5

FT-61.   Complete the table for the equation $y = x – 5$, then graph the equation on the same axes you used in the previous problem.

input	-2	-1	0	1	3	6	x
output							x – 5

FT-62.   Complete the scale for each part below.

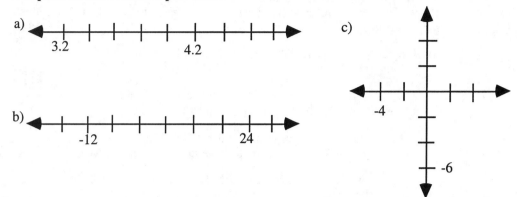

a)
3.2   4.2

b)
-12   24

c)
-4
-6

FT-63.   After looking at his partner's graph, shown at right, Jung suggested that his partner check his work. Why did Jung think that a mistake had been made?

FT-64.   Jon's test score was 84 correct out of 100 possible. Write his score as a percent.

FT-65.   In order for Bailey's Bowling Club to compete in the bowling championships, their top ten scores must average 260. Their scores were 251, 256, 229, 209, 257, 258, 265, 243, 258, and 278.

a)   What is the mean (average)?

b)   Will the bowling club go to the championships? Explain how you know.

FT-66.   Follow your teacher's directions for practicing mental math. What strategy did you use today?

FT-67. Today your team decided to hike to the top of Lookout Point. Take out your "Big Tree Park" resource page to help you answer the following questions.

a) What is the elevation at the campsite? At Lookout Point? At sea level?

b) If you started the hike from the campsite and you are now at sea level, how far have you hiked?

c) If it has taken one hour to hike this far, how much elevation gain have you made per minute?

d) Since you are at sea level (elevation = 0 feet), how much elevation would you have gained after one minute of hiking? After two minutes?

e) Two minutes from now is represented by positive two. How is one minute ago represented?

f) What was the elevation one minute ago? Two minutes ago?

g) Copy the following table and find the y-values for each elevation.

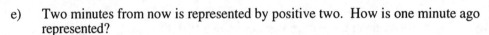

	Minutes Ago					Now	Minutes from Now					
Time in Minutes (x)	-10	-5	-4	-3	-2	-1	0	1	2	3	4	5	10
Elevation in Feet (y)							0						

h) Graph the information from the table. Put "time in minutes" on the horizontal (x) axis and "elevation in feet" on the vertical (y) axis. Scale both axes so one tick mark represents one unit (go up by ones). Then complete parts (i) through (m).

i) Use complete sentences to describe the pattern you see in the gain in elevation. Use this pattern to find the gain in elevation after 10 minutes of hiking.

j) Write the equation that describes the pattern.

k) What is the range in elevation from the campsite to Lookout Point?

l) How long will it take to reach Lookout Point?

m) Use your Tool Kit and check to see that your graph is complete. Write "My graph is complete" on your paper.

T-68. The equation $y = 2x$ describes how y is related to x in the hiking problem.

a) Use the resource page to complete the table below exactly as shown. Use the table from the previous problem and your graph to help you.

x (time in minutes)	2(x)	y (elevation in feet)
25	2(25)	50
10	2(10)	
5		
3		
0		
-3		
-5		
-10		
-25		

b) What is true about the integers you multiplied to get a positive product?

c) What is true about the integers you multiplied to get a negative product?

T-69. Copy and complete each table. Then explain the pattern between the input and output values using complete sentences. Finally, write the equation (rule) that describes the pattern.

a)

in (x)	28		6	0	15				360
out (y)	14	12	3		7.5	9	410		

b)

x	4	2	0			14	102
y	11	5	-1	8	20		

T-70. Copy and complete the table below using values from -4 to 4 for the rule $y = 2x + 4$.

x (in)	-4	-3	-2	-1	0	1	2	3	4
y (out)									

a) Graph the information from the table.

b) Find the x- and y-intercepts.

c) Use your Tool Kit to make sure your graph is complete. When it is complete, write "My graph is complete" on your paper.

T-71. Sketch a tile drawing and write an equation. Some problems will require you to add zero pairs.

a) 7 – 3   b) -6 – (-9)

c) 5 + (-8)   d) -9 + 16

e) 6 – 9   f) 12 – (-5)

FT-72. Find the missing number that will make each equation true. Model your solution after the example in part (a).

a) $x + 8 = 24$
    $16 + 8 = 24$
    $x = 16$

b) $12 + z = 7$

c) $17 - w = 8$

d) $25 = g + (-5)$

FT-73. Answer the questions below.

a) What is the length of the horizontal side of the rectangle? How long is the height?

b) Calculate the area.

c) Calculate the perimeter.

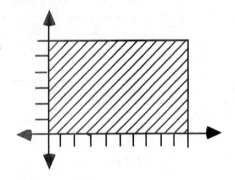

FT-74. A full-grown ostrich weighs 345 pounds and stands 108 inches tall. Irving weighs 112 pounds and is 5 feet tall. About how many times heavier than Irving is the ostrich? About how many feet taller than Irving is it?

FT-75. Simplify and select the correct answer to $3 - 7 + 4 - 2$.

(A) -3   (B) -2   (C) 1   (D) 5   (E) none of these

FT-76. At the end of a 147-mile trip, Pat's car had been driven a total of 3,835 miles. How many miles had the car already been driven at the beginning of her trip?

(A) 2,688   (B) 3,588   (C) 3,688   (D) 3,982   (E) none of these

FT-77. The hikers are on their way back to camp from Lookout Point. Their elevation is dropping at the rate of about three feet per minute. The equation $y = -3x$ represents the speed at which they are losing elevation.

a) If the hikers had started at sea level (elevation = 0 feet), what would be their elevation after one minute of hiking downhill? After two minutes?

b) Copy and complete the section of the table below for "Minutes in the Future."

		Minutes ago					Now		Minutes in the Future				
x (minutes)	-10	-5	-4	-3	-2	-1	0	1	2	3	4	5	x
y (feet)							0	-3					

c) What kind of integers did you use to represent the elevation for "minutes in the future"?

d) What do you notice about the change in elevation?

e) If the hikers start at an elevation of 0 and continue to hike at the same rate, how long will it take them to reach the camp site?

f) If "now" is represented by 0, how is 1 minute ago represented? 2 minutes ago?

g) Go back and complete your table for "minutes ago." What was the elevation 1 minute ago? 2 minutes ago?

h) What kind of integers did you use to represent the elevation for minutes ago?

i) Graph the times and elevations from the table. Be sure to label your axes and show your scaling. Put "time" in minutes on the horizontal (x) axis and "elevation" in feet on the vertical (y) axis. Scale the x-axis by ones. Scale the y-axis by threes.

j) Extend the line as far as you can on your graph.

k) Use your table or the equation $y = -3x$ to find the elevation after 10 minutes of hiking; after 30 minutes of hiking.

FT-78. Refer to your table in the previous problem and your map of Big Tree Park.

a) Describe how the pattern in the table is related to the equation $y = -3x$.

b) What is the range in elevation from Lookout Point to camp?

c) Use either the pattern from your table or the equation to find out how long it will take the hikers to get from Lookout Point back to camp.

FT-79. The equation $y = -3x$ describes how y is related to x.

a) Copy and complete the table below. Complete the table exactly as shown. Use the patterns from the previous problems or your graph to help you.

x (minutes)	-3(x)	y (elevation in feet)
25	-3(25)	
10	-3(10)	
5		
3		-9
0		
-3		9
-5		
-10		
-25		

b) What is true about the integers you multiplied to get a positive product?

c) What is true about the integers you multiplied to get a negative product?

FT-80. While on their hikes, students collected some tadpole specimens from the pond. The tadpoles were just beginning to develop legs. The lengths of the legs they measured were 0.45 cm, 1.3 cm, 3.1 cm, 0.78 cm, and 2.3 cm.

a) Find the range.   b) Find the mean.

FT-81. Students collected one specimen of tadpoles on Monday, Tuesday, and Wednesday. Tuesday's specimen included 13 tadpoles more than the specimen from Monday. Wednesday's specimen included 27 fewer than Monday's. The total number of tadpoles collected was 1273.

a) Set up a Guess and Check table to find out how many tadpoles students collected on Monday.

b) Solve the problem using Guess and Check. Write your answer in a complete sentence.

FT-82. Here is a different section of the number line. Once again, Irving needs help. Show him what numbers are needed to correctly label each tick mark on the number line.

-15   0

a) What is the largest number on this part of the number line?

b) What is the smallest number on this part of the number line?

c) Tell Irving how he can use the number line to determine which of the two numbers is larger than the other.

FT-83. Solve for x.

a) $|-15| = x$ b) $|x| = 5$

c) $|x| = -7$ d) $|x| = 28$

FT-84. Mrs. Poppington corrected more tests. Here are the scores:
51, 54, 55, 55, 62, 63, 65, 72, 76, 78, 79, 81, 82, 83, 85, 86, 91, 93, and 95. Find:

a) the median.   b) the upper quartile.

c) the lower quartile.   d) Put the data in a box-and-whisker plot.

FT-85. Complete the following Diamond Problems.

Product

Sum

a)   b)   c)   d)   e)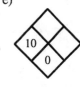

-3   -4   -2   - 3   0.2   0.3   7   -6   10

0

FT-86.   Use integer tiles to help you solve the following problems. Sketch the tile drawing and
          write the equation for each problem.

a)   -6 – 9   b)   -6 + (-9)

c)   5 – 7   d)   5 + (-7)

e)   7 – (-3)   f)   7 + 3

g)   Compare your equation in part (a) to your equation in part (b).
      i)   How are they similar?
      ii)   How are they different?

h)   Compare your equation in part (c) to your equation in part (d).
      i)   How are they similar?
      ii)   How are they different?

i)   Compare your equation in part (e) to your equation in part (f).
      i)   How are they similar?
      ii)   How are they different?

j)   Follow the examples in parts (a) through (f) above and rewrite the subtraction
      problem 12 – (-7) as an addition problem.

Narrator:	*After doing several subtraction problems with integers, Lacy exclaimed:*
Lacy:	"I've found a shortcut! I don't need to subtract. I can just add!"
Narrator:	*Her friend, Ida, who did not really like subtraction, shouted:*
Ida:	"What do you mean? Can you teach it to me?"
Narrator:	*Lacy replied:*
Lacy:	"Sure Ida, I'd be happy to. How about 3 – 5? If you were using tiles, how many zero pairs would you add?"
Ida:	"I would add two zero pairs, then take away the five positives, and combine, just like the problem says, 3 – 5. My answer is negative two."
Lacy:	"Me too, Ida. That's how I would do it if I didn't use the addition shortcut. Let's try it my way.
	"Start with three positive tiles. Then add in five negative tiles. Now circle the zero pairs and count up the tiles left over.
	"See, there are two negative tiles left over. I got the same answer as you did, negative two.
	I noticed that 3 – (5) has the same answer as 3 + (-5) so that's what I do. I just **add the opposite of the second number**, circle the zeros, and get the same answer as you."
Narrator:	*With that, Ida exclaimed:*
Ida:	"When subtracting integers, all I have to do is **add the opposite**!"
	"If the problem says 1 – 6, I can rewrite it as 1 + (-6) and I get the same answer both times. 1 – 6 = (-5) and 1+ (-6) = (-5)."

FT-87. Rewrite each of the following subtraction problems as addition of the opposite. Then compute the answer.

a) $4 - 9$

b) $5 - 7$

c) $-12 - 2$

FT-88.

```
┌─────────────────────────────────────────────────────────────────┐
│              RULE FOR SUBTRACTING INTEGERS                        │
│                                                                   │
│   Adding the opposite of the second number gives the same         │
│   answer as subtracting it.                                       │
│                                                                   │
│   Step One:    Change the subtraction sign to an addition sign.   │
│                                                                   │
│   Step Two:    Change the sign of the integer you are subtracting.│
│                                                                   │
│   Step Three:  Use the integer rules for addition.                │
│                                                                   │
│   Here is an example: 4 – (-5) = 4 + (+5) = 9.                     │
└─────────────────────────────────────────────────────────────────┘
```

Put two examples of subtracting integers to the right of the double-lined box in your Tool Kit. One example must have at least one negative integer. When you return to class, have your partner or a teammate check that your examples are correct.

FT-89. Complete each subtraction problem.

a) $2 - 4$

b) $6 - (-2)$

c) $-7 - (-20)$

FT-90. Complete the tables for each equation. Then graph the equations on the <u>same set of axes</u>.

a) $y = x - 4$

in (x)	-3	-2	-1	0	1	2	3	x
out (y)								

b) $y = x^2$ Hint: x^2 means "x times x."

in (x)	-3	-2	-1	0	1	2	3	x
out (y)								

c) Describe any difference(s) you see in the two graphs in relation to their equations.

FT-91.   Copy and complete the tables below using each value of x given.

a)   y = 4x

x	y
3	4(3) = 12
2	
1	
0	
-1	
-2	4(-2) = -8
-3	

b)   y = -4x

x	y
3	-4(3) = -12
2	
1	
0	
-1	
-2	(-4)(-2) = 8
-3	

c)   Use a different color for each equation and graph both of them on the <u>same</u> <u>set</u> <u>of</u> <u>axes</u>. Scale the x-axis from -3 to 3 and the y-axis from -12 to 12.

d)   What is the same about these two graphs? What is different?

e)   Look carefully at the two equations in parts (a) and (b). What do you think determines which way the line slants?

FT-92.   Exchange binders with your partner. (If you do not have time in class for this binder check, have someone at home do this check with you.)

a)   Are there labeled sections?

b)   Without actually performing the "shake test," do you think your partner's binder would survive the test? Estimate how many papers or objects might fall out.

c)   Write down one suggestion for how your partner might better organize his/her binder.

FT-93.   Refer to the table in problem FT-79. Use it to copy and complete the following statements.

a)   When you multiply two positive numbers, the product will be _____.

b)   When you multiply two negative numbers, the product will be _____.

c)   When you multiply one positive and one negative number, the product will be _____ .

FT-94.   Mrs. Poppington is trying to decide whether to require everyone to retake the Chapter 1 test. The class scores on the first test were 0, 14, 42, 63, 75, 88, 90, and 90.

a)   Calculate the mean, median, and mode.

b)   Using one of the above measures of central tendency, argue the following case: You scored 90 on the first test and want to keep your score, so you argue against a retest.

c)   Using one of the above measures of central tendency, argue the following case: You scored 14 on the test and know you can improve your score if you take the test again, so you argue for the retest.

FT-95.   At right is another section of a number line, and Irving is still confused. He does not see which number is larger. Finish scaling this section and try another approach to help him.

Irving can use the < (less than) or the > (greater than) symbols to order the numbers you wrote. Remember that the pointed part of the symbol points to the smaller number, and the open part opens toward the larger number.

less than symbol   **greater than symbol**

Use the < and > symbols to complete the following inequalities.

a)   2 ___ 3   b)   -2 ___ 3   c)   -3 ___ -17   d)   -17 ___ 3

FT-96.   Set up tables using values from -3 to 3 for x and graph the following two equations.

a) $y = 2x - 4$ b) $y = x^2 + 1$

FT-97.   Write a numerical equation that represent each statement.

a)   A number x multiplied by three equals negative forty-eight.

b)   Negative seven added to a number y equals negative twenty-four.

c)   Negative six subtracted from a number r is equal to seventeen.

d)   When negative twelve is subtracted from a number x the result is four.

FT-98. Logan, who is in third grade, asked his older sister, Adrianne, what "3 · 4" means.

    a) Using complete sentences, explain how Adrianne could help Logan understand what "3 · 4" means.

    b) Draw a picture that Adrianne could use to show Logan what "3 · 4" means.

    c) Give a real-life example of when you might use "3 · 4."

FT-99. Compute.

    a) $(-2) \cdot (-6)$ b) $(-10) \cdot (-5)$ c) $(-4) \cdot (-7)$ d) $8 \cdot 5$

    e) $4 \cdot (-4)$ f) $(-3) \cdot 6$ g) $3 \cdot (-8)$ h) $2 \cdot (-11)$

FT-100. Check your solutions to the previous problem with your partner. If you have different answers, check with another pair of students. If you still disagree, get a calculator and check again. Correct any errors you may have made. If you made no errors, write "No Errors for Problem FT-99" on your paper for this problem.

FT-101. Use your answers from problem FT-99 to answer the following questions.

    a) Look at the sign of the answers for parts (a) through (d). They should all be the same. What do all of the problems have in common?

    b) Look at the sign of the answers for parts (e) through (h). They should all be the same. What do all of the problems have in common?

FT-102. Write the multiplication sentence and the product that go with each drawing below.

    a)
```
- - - - -
- - - - -
- - - - -
```
    b)
```
- - - - - - -
- - - - - - -
- - - - - - -
- - - - - - -
- - - - - - -
- - - - - - -
```
    c)
```
- - - -
- - - -
- - - -
- - - -
- - - -
```

FT-103. In the previous problems, you used the integer tiles and drawings to calculate products of integers. When you multiplied, you were adding groups of negative tiles. For example, if the problem was 3(-2), you added three groups of negative two.

a) Copy and complete the table below.

Problem	Sentence	Answer
4(-5)	Add 4 groups of -5	-20
5(-4)	Add ____ groups of ____	
6(-7)	Add ____ groups of ____	

b) Complete the sentence: Multiplication is repeated _____ .

c) What does (-3)(6) represent?

FT-104. Use tiles to find each product. Make a drawing of your work. Write the solution as an equation. Remember that the first number tells you how many groups there are and the second number tells you how many are in each group.

a) 3(-4)   b) 5(-2)   c) 4(-1)   d) 6(2)

FT-105. At right is a way to multiply using integer tiles in a situation in which the first integer is negative. Consider the problem (-4)(3).

a) Draw a large **neutral field**; that is, draw several pairs of positive and negative tiles. Circle and remove one group of +3. Do it again. Do it again. Do it one more time. How many times did you remove groups of +3?

b) Since multiplication shows a repeated process, the steps done in part (a) showed the problem (-4)(+3). The sentence describing the multiplication problem would be "Remove four groups of positive three." What result did you get?

FT-106. Using integer tiles, draw a large neutral field and use the same process as you did in the preceding problem.

a) Show (-5)(3). Complete the sentence: "Remove ____ groups of ____ ."

b) Show (-7)(2). Complete the sentence: "Remove ____ groups of ____ ."

c) When both integers are negative, you perform the same steps, but you remove the negative tiles. Copy this example: (-4)(-2) means "Remove four groups of -2 tiles." Copy the drawing at right, and indicate that the result is 8.

FT-107. Copy and complete the following multiplication table.

Drawing	Product	What is left
+ + + + + + + + (-)(-)(-)	(-3)(-3)	
+ + + + + + + + (-)(-) - - -		
+ + + + + + + + (-)(-)(-)(-)-		

FT-108.

RULES FOR MULTIPLYING INTEGERS

If you multiply two integers with the **same sign**, the answer is **positive**.

If you multiply two integers with **different signs**, the answer is **negative**.

Examples: $(3)(5) = 15$; $(-3)(5) = -15$; $(-3)(-5) = 15$

Put two examples of multiplying integers to the right of the double-lined box in your Tool Kit. One example must have at least one negative integer. When you return to class, have your partner or a teammate check that your examples are correct.

FT-109. Copy each problem and compute the product.

a) $(-3)(6)$

b) $(-7)(-3)$

c) $(-7)(-7)$

d) $(5)(-6)$

e) $(9)(-2)$

f) $(-12)(-1)$

FT-110. Copy each problem and compute the sum.

a) $-3 + 12$

b) $10 + (-7)$

c) $12 + (-4)$

FT-111. Rewrite each subtraction problem as an addition problem and compute the sum.

a) $-6 - (-12)$

b) $7 - (-10)$

c) $4 - 10$

FT-112. As your class was hiking, you noticed small herds of deer. The list below shows how many deer you have seen each day.

Monday................ 12
Tuesday 7
Wednesday 8
Thursday 9
Friday 15
Saturday 8

a) Determine the mean.

b) Determine the median.

c) Determine the mode.

d) Find the range for the sightings of the deer.

FT-113. Compute. Be sure to show all your work.

a) $5.62 \cdot 0.23$

b) $71.234 + 2.36 + 0.425$

c) $6.254 - 4.91$

FT-114. Complete the Diamond Problems below.

Product

Sum

a)

b)

c)

d)

e)

FT-115. Use the < and > symbols to complete the inequalities below.

a) $0.33 \_\_ 50\%$ b) $\frac{1}{4} \_\_ 0.20$ c) $67\% \_\_ 0.65$ d) $\frac{3}{4} \_\_ 72\%$

FT-116.   The prices for a Zippy convertible are listed in the
           newspaper as shown below to the right.

           a)   Write the data as six ordered pairs. Be careful.

           b)   What information will you plot on the x-axis?

           c)   What information will you plot on the y-axis?

           d)   Scale your axes.

           e)   Create a graph and plot the data.

Year	Price
2000	$38,500
1999	$31,000
1998	$26,000
1997	$22,000
1996	$18,500
1995	$15,900

FT-117.   Follow your teacher's instructions for practicing mental math. What new strategy did
           you use today?

FT-118.   At right is an example of a number family. Notice that each equation
           contains the same three numbers.

           $3 \cdot 4 = 12$
           $4 \cdot 3 = 12$
           $12 \div 3 = 4$
           $12 \div 4 = 3$

           Follow the same format and write number families for the equations
           below.

           a) $6 \cdot 3 = 18$ b) $2 \cdot 5 = 10$

FT-119.   Complete each of the following number families.

           a) $-7 \cdot 2 = -14$ b) $-6 \cdot (-4) = 24$

           c) $8 \cdot (-1) = -8$ d) $9 \cdot 5 = 45$

           e)   What is true about the signs of the integers you divided to get a positive quotient
                 above?

           f)   What is true about the signs of the integers you divided to get a negative quotient
                 above?

FT-120.

RULES FOR DIVIDING INTEGERS

The rules for determining the sign of the answer for division of integers are the **same as multiplication.**

If you divide two integers with the **same sign**, the answer is **positive**.

If you divide two integers with **different signs**, the answer is **negative.**

Examples: $6 \div 2 = 3$; $\frac{-8}{4} = -2$

Make these notes in your Tool Kit to the right of the double-lined box.

List two examples of dividing integers. One example must have at least one negative integer. Have your partner or a teammate check that your examples are correct.

FT-121. Find the value of each expression.

a) $(-21) \div 7$ b) $(-42) \div (-6)$ c) $28 \div (-4)$ d) $(-63) \div (-7)$

FT-122. Copy and complete the table using each value of x given or use the resource page. Be sure to follow the example problem and show all your steps. The answers are in the table so you can check your work. Correct any entries that you get wrong.

a) Graph the points from the table. Make sure you have followed all the steps for making a complete graph.

b) Describe the graph you made.

x	$y = x^2 + 1$
3	$3^2 + 1$ $(3)(3) + 1$ $9 + 1$ 10
2	
0	
-2	

FT-123. Use what you have learned about integer addition and subtraction to rewrite the following subtraction problems as addition problems and compute the sums.

a) $-15 - (-8)$ b) $18 - (-10)$

c) $-6 - 10$ d) $12 - (14)$

FT-124. Copy each problem and compute the answer for the indicated operation.

a) $-27 \div 9$ b) $-10 + (-5)$ c) $3 - 9$ d) $-20 + 8$

e) $(-4)(7)$ f) $(-6)(-5)$ g) $12 \div (-3)$ h) $-6 + 5 - (-6)$

FT-125.   Copy and complete the table using the equation $y = 3x - 2$.

x (in)	-2	-1	0	1	2	x
y (out)						

a)   If you were to graph the points from the table, what would you expect the graph to look like?

b)   Graph the points. Make sure your graph is complete.

c)   What does your graph look like? Does this agree with your prediction in part (a)?

FT-126.   Use the graph at right to:

a)   Copy the ordered pairs for each point into an xy-table.

b)   Write the rule using a complete sentence.

c)   Name the x- and y-intercepts.

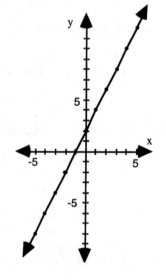

FT-127.   Find the number that will make each number sentence true.

a) $x + 8 = 6$ b) $x + (-4) = 7$ c) $4a = 36$ d) $x - (-7) = 5$

FT-128.   Study the following tables to determine the pattern used. Write the equation in y-form for each table. Explain how you determined the rule.

a)

x	1	2	3	4	5	6	x
y	-1	-4	-7	-10	-13	-16	

b)

x	-5	-4	-3	-2	-1	0	1	2	3	x
y	-8	-6	-4	-2	0	2	4	6	8	

c)

x	-4	-3	-2	-1	0	1	2	3	4	x
y	16	9	4	1	0	1	4	9	16	

FT-129.   In the following problem two groups will be hiking. Be
          prepared to make a prediction about both groups. This
          problem will take some time. Once you have followed all of
          the directions for one group you will repeat the process for the
          second group.

          The Big Hike   At Big Tree Park, Raul, the park ranger, and
          Mia, the chief naturalist, each led a group hike. Raul's group
          hiked to Grizzly Peak, which has an elevation of 182 feet.
          Mia's group hiked to Mt. Sawtooth, which has an elevation of
          324 feet. The elevation of their campsite is 120 feet below sea
          level. If Mia's group hikes downhill at a rate of 3 feet per
          minute and Raul's group hikes downhill at a rate of 2 feet per
          minute, predict which group will arrive at the campsite first.

FT-130.   Answer the following subproblems for Raul's hiking group.

     a)   If they have not yet started hiking, what is the elevation of Raul's group now?

     b)   If "x" represents minutes spent hiking and "y" represents elevation in feet, write an
          ordered pair to represent Raul's group now. (Remember they have not started
          hiking yet.)

     c)   What is the elevation of Raul's group after one minute of hiking? two minutes?
          three minutes? Write an ordered pair to represent each situation.

     d)   Write a variable expression to represent the rate of descent as feet per minute for
          Raul's group. (How fast are they hiking downhill?)

     e)   Obtain the resource page from your teacher and complete the table for Raul's group
          for the first five minutes of hiking. Leave the rest of the table blank for now.

     f)   Use your table and what you have learned from playing silent board games to find
          the rule for Raul's group.

     g)   Follow the example on the resource page and use the rule for Raul's group to
          calculate the remaining values in the table. Use these values to complete your table.

     h)   Graph the information from the table starting with their elevation now and using all
          the remaining values you calculated. (Multiples of five minutes.)

     i)   Draw a continuous line through the points you graphed.

     j)   Find the range in elevation from Grizzly Peak to the campsite.

     k)   At a rate of descent of two feet per minute, how long will it take Raul's hiking
          group to reach camp?

     l)   According to your graph, how many minutes did it take Raul's group to reach their
          campsite? Does this agree with your answer in part (k)? Explain.

FT-131.   Repeat all of the above subproblems for Mia's hiking group.

FT-132.   Which group reached camp first? Does this agree with your prediction?

FT-133.   **Chapter Summary** As you finish a chapter, you
           need to reflect on how well you know the material.
           Here is another way to check your understanding at the
           end of a chapter.

    a)   Find a problem in the chapter that represents what
           you have learned about each of the following
           topics. Copy the problem and show the correct
           solution for the problem.

           • Solve a word problem using a Guess and
             Check table.

           • Write an equation based on a table.

           • Graph a linear equation.

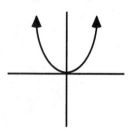

    b)   Make up two problems for each operation (+, −, ·, ÷) with integers and show how to
           solve your problems. Be sure to use some negative numbers.

FT-134.   Match each equation to the graph it best fits. Explain how you made your decisions.

    a) $y = 2x + 2$ b) $y = x^2$ c) $y = -2x$

    i)   ii)   iii)

FT-135.   A graph is represented by the equation $y = x^2 - 1$.

    a)   Complete the following data table using the equation.

in (x)	-3	-2	-1	0	1	2	3	x
out (y)								

    b)   On a graph, plot the values from the data table above.

FT-136. Copy and complete the table using each value of x given. Be sure to follow the example problem and **show all your steps**. The answers are in the table so you can check your solutions. Correct any that you get wrong.

x	$y = x^2 - 2$
3	$3^2 - 2$ $(3)(3) - 2$ $9 - 2$ 7
2	2
1	-1
0	-2
-1	-1
-2	2
-3	7

FT-137. Do the following computations.

a) $-15 + 9$

b) $2 + (-5) - 7$

c) $-10 \cdot (-2)$

d) $9 - (-22)$

e) $7 \cdot (-4)$

f) $-4 + 9 - (-31)$

g) $-24 \div 3$

h) $230 \div 10$

i) $-52 \div (-13)$

FT-138. Write a numerical equation that represents each statement.

a) When seven is added to a number x, the result is three.

b) When a number a is doubled, the result is twelve.

c) When negative six is subtracted from a number y, the result is eighteen.

d) When a number n is divided by seven, the result is negative two.

FT-139. Look back at your work from this chapter.

a) Write the equations from three graphs that made straight lines.

b) Write the equations from three graphs that made curves.

c) How can you tell what kind of equation will give which kind of graph?

FT-140.   **What We Have Done in This Chapter**

Below is a list of the Tool Kit entries from this chapter.

- FT-19   Graphing Terms
- FT-45   Components of a Linear Graph
- FT-50   Addition of Integers
- FT-88   Rule for Subtracting Integers
- FT-108   Rules for Multiplying Integers
- FT-120   Rules for Dividing Integers

Review all the entries and read the notes you made in your Tool Kit. Make a list of any questions, terms, or notes you do not understand. Ask your partner or study team members for help. If anything is still unclear, ask your teacher.

THE MYSTERY OF THE Dual Spinners

Chapter 3

Chapter 3
Mystery of the Dual Spinners: **PROBABILITY AND FRACTIONS**

Every day you use **probability** to make decisions. Any question that starts with "What is the chance of ..." or "Should I do ..." is a question that involves probability, whether you consciously use probability or not. As you make your decisions, you are probably also using fractions or percents. As you continue to use numbers, you soon find that there are many situations that cannot be completely described only with whole numbers. Fractions, decimals, and percents are ways to describe parts of things; they are the "numbers between the integers." As you work with these kinds of numbers, you will dual learn how to add, subtract, and multiply them.

In this chapter you will have the opportunity to:

- use ideas from probability to gain a new perspective on addition and multiplication of fractions.

- build your understanding of addition and multiplication of fractions through the use of rectangular area models.

- review equivalent fractions and simplification of fractions.

- review the relationships among fractions, decimals, and percents.

Read the problem below, but **do not try to solve it now**. What you learn over the next few days will enable you to solve it.

MD-0.　Mario and Marisa Powers are twins. For as long as they can remember, they have wanted to be federal investigators when they grow up. To their surprise, they were picked to be junior interns at the National Investigative Agency (N.I.A.) headed by Delano Franklin.

"For the final exam I will assess your skills through a color combo bingo game," said Director Franklin. "You will use a game card while I use two dice. You will need to make a prediction based on which color combinations you think will occur most often."

How should the twins label their card?

Number Sense		
Algebra and Functions		
Mathematical Reasoning		
Measurement and Geometry		
Statistics, Data Analysis, & Probability		

Chapter 3
Mystery of the Dual Spinners: PROBABILITY AND FRACTIONS

MD-1.   Make a number line on your paper and place the problem letter (a, b, c...) in a position that corresponds to the probability of the event happening. Part (a) is done as an example.

0   **a**   1

a)   It will rain today. (The reporter states there is a 50% chance of rain).

b)   A Martian will walk into class now.

c)   You will eat some vegetables for dinner today.

d)   You will pass your math class this year.

e)   You will breathe in the next 30 seconds.

f)   You will be elected president.

MD-2.   Because of their great problem solving skills and inquisitive minds, Mario and Marisa Powers were picked to be junior interns at the National Investigative Agency (N.I.A.) headed by Delano Franklin.

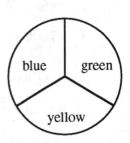

"The first thing we want to do is assess your intuition through a color combo bingo game," said Director Franklin. "Here's how to play.

"Use a game card while I use two spinners like the ones below. After you read the game directions and study the spinners, you will need to make a predictionas to which color combination you think will occur most often. Then you will label both sides of the 16 squares according to your predictions."

Your teacher will give you a resource page so that you can play Director Franklin's color combination game.

blue | blue
green

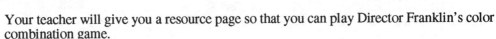

blue | green
yellow

>>Problem continues on the next page.>>

a) List the combinations that are possible.

b) Predict the color combination(s) you think will occur most often. Record these predictions.

c) On the game card your teacher has given you label both parts of the 16 squares according to your predictions. You will need to repeat some of the combinations in order to fill all 16 squares.

Color-Combo-Grido I
A game for many people.

Mathematical Purpose: To study mathematical probability.

Object: To cover four squares in a row or to cover the entire game board.

Materials:
• 4 x 4 grid with squares divided in two parts.
• two spinners divided into three equal parts: Spinner 1 parts labeled blue, blue, and green; Spinner 2 parts labeled blue, green, and yellow.
• two paper clips to use as spinners, if needed

Scoring: One point for the four-in-a-row game; five points for a cover game.

How to Play the Game:
• Label all 16 squares with color combinations
• Caller spins both spinners and calls out colors.
• Circle one square matching the combination called (blue/yellow and yellow/blue are considered the same).
• Circle only color combinations that match the call.
• Keep track of each play by tallying each color combination called.

Ending the Game: The first person with four squares in a row (horizontal, vertical, or diagonal) wins; or, the first person with his/her entire card marked out wins.

MD-3. After collecting class information, answer these questions:

a) Which color combination occurred most often in your team?

b) Which color combination occurred most often in your class?

c) If you played the game 1000 times, Blue-Green will probably occur the most often. Why do you think this is true?

MD-4. Director Franklin then explained to the twins that they would be using disguises of sunglasses and hats when on assignment. "Cool!" exclaimed Mario, "We're not allowed to wear either one at school."

Marissa

Mario

"We'll use a pair of spinners to decide who wears which disguise. Use your resource page, a paper clip, and a pencil to begin collecting data."

First spin Marisa's spinner and then spin Mario's. Four possible combinations will occur. On your resource page, use tally marks to keep a record of how often each combination comes up. Do this 25 times. (You will have 25 tally marks recorded in your table.) In <u>this</u> experiment, <u>order</u> <u>is</u> <u>important</u>.

How many times did the spinners give you each of the disguise combinations, that is, "Glasses-Glasses," "Glasses-Hat," "Hat-Glasses," or "Hat-Hat"?

MD-5.

PROBABILITY

When you know all possible outcomes of an event, and all have the same chance of occurring, the probability of an event is:

$$P(event) = \frac{\text{number of outcomes in the event}}{\text{number of possible outcomes}}$$

P(event) is the way we write that we want the probability "P" of a certain event. For example, there are 6 faces on a die. Suppose the desired event is to roll a 4. Since the number 4 appears once, we write the probability of getting a 4 as $P(4) = \frac{1}{6}$.

Make these notes in your Tool Kit to the right of the double-lined box.

a) Highlight the "P(event) = " statement.

b) Write the probability of getting an odd number if you roll a die.

MD-6.   Use the information from the Tool Kit box on probability
and the results from your "Disguises" spinning
experiment to answer the following questions.

a)   About how many "Glasses-Glasses" results would
you expect after 50 spins?

b)   Write the probability of getting the "Glasses-
Glasses" combination based on your prediction for
50 spins.

c)   About how many "Hat-Hat" results would you expect after 75 spins?

d)   Write the probability of getting the "Hat-Hat" combination based on your prediction
for 75 spins.

e)   Write the probability of getting either the "Glasses-Hat" or the "Hat-Glasses"
combination based on 125 spins.

f)   Use complete sentences to explain your reasoning in part (e).

MD-7.   Copy and complete the following multiplication table or use the resource page.

x	-5	-4	-3	-2	-1	0	1	2	3
-5									
-4									
-3									
-2									
-1									
0									
1									
2									
3									

MD-8.   The least common multiple of 10 and 12 is:

(A) 2   (B) 30   (C) 60   (D) 120   (E) none of these

MD-9.   The result of combining the three fractions $1\frac{1}{8} + \frac{1}{8} - \frac{5}{4}$ is:

(A) -1   (B) 0   (C) $\frac{5}{8}$ (D) $\frac{4}{5}$ (E) none of these

MD-10.   Now that we have started a new chapter, it is time for you to organize your binder.

a)   Put the work from the last chapter in order and keep it in a separate folder.

b)   When this is completed, write, "I have organized my binder."

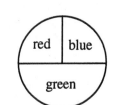

MD-11.   Follow your teacher's directions for practicing mental math. There are several ways to do the problem. Which method do you think was best?

MD-12.   Marisa found the spinner at right in a box of discarded game pieces.

a)   What is the probability that she would spin red?

b)   What is the probability that she would spin blue?

c)   What is the probability that she would spin green?

d)   Explain how you determined your answers.

MD-13.   Your teacher will give you additional data from other classes for the Color-Combo-Grido and the Hat-Glasses spinners.

a)   Compare the new numbers to your previous results. Write your numbers as fractions.

b)   Do you see any differences in the data?

MD-14.   Director Delano Franklin owns four kinds of motor vehicles. Each type comes in two different colors. Marisa and Mario had to spin for the vehicle that they would use while out on investigations. Use the two spinners to answer the questions below.

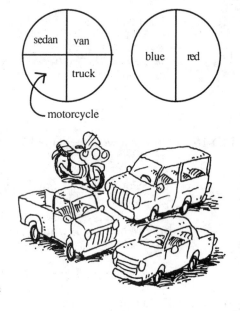

a)   List eight possible vehicle-color combinations. Start with SB for blue sedan.

b)   Does the first spin to select the type of vehicle have any effect on the results of the second spin to select the vehicle's color?

c)   What is the probability of spinning a red motorcycle?

d)   What is the probability of spinning a blue van?

e)   What is the probability of spinning a blue vehicle?

MD-15.   Another way of looking at the previous problem is to use a rectangle to display the choices. The area of the rectangle represents the <u>sum</u> of the possibilities, that is, the sum of the fractional probabilities is 1. This means that the area of the rectangle equals one (1) square unit.

a)   The first spinner was divided into four equal parts, so draw a rectangle and divide it vertically into four equal columns to represent the different vehicles. Label the top of each section with the name of a different vehicle.

b)   The second spinner is divided into two equal parts, so divide your rectangle horizontally into two equal rows to represent the different colors. Label each row with a different color.

c)   How many equal parts are there in the rectangle?

d)   If you carefully divided the rectangle into four equal columns and two equal rows, what is the area of each section of the rectangle?

e)   What is the probability of spinning each combination? Write that fraction in each section of the rectangle.

f)   What is the relationship between the area of each section of the rectangle and the probability of getting that color combination?

MD-16.   Travis prefers to drive blue vehicles. He also likes to drive vans, sedans, or trucks. Use the probability rectangle below to answer these questions.

	$\frac{1}{4}$ Van	$\frac{1}{4}$ Sedan	$\frac{1}{4}$ Truck	$\frac{1}{4}$ Motorcycle
$\frac{1}{2}$ Blue	$\frac{1}{8}$	$\frac{1}{8}$	$\frac{1}{8}$	$\frac{1}{8}$
$\frac{1}{2}$ Red	$\frac{1}{8}$	$\frac{1}{8}$	$\frac{1}{8}$	$\frac{1}{8}$

a)   What is the probability that he gets a vehicle he likes?

b)   What is the probability that he gets a vehicle of a color or type he does not like?

c)   What is the probability that the color of the vehicle he drives is green?

MD-17.   The third term in the pattern below, based on $\frac{1}{3}$, is $\frac{3}{9}$:

$$\frac{1}{3} \cdot \frac{1}{1} = \frac{1}{3}; \qquad \frac{1}{3} \cdot \frac{2}{2} = \frac{2}{6}; \qquad \frac{1}{3} \cdot \frac{3}{3} = \frac{3}{9}$$

a)   What is the third term of a similar pattern based on $\frac{1}{2}$?

b)   What is the fourth term of a similar pattern based on $\frac{2}{3}$? Explain how you found it.

c)   What is the fifth term of a similar pattern based on $\frac{3}{4}$? Explain how you found it.

d)   If a pattern is based on $\frac{4}{5}$, predict the tenth term.

MD-18.   Using the idea of finding patterns in the previous problem, find the unknown number in each problem below.

a) $\frac{3}{5} = \frac{12}{x}$ b) $\frac{9}{18} = \frac{w}{6}$

MD-19.   Complete the following Diamond Problems.

Product

Sum

a)

b)

c)

d)

e)

f)

MD-20.   Draw a rectangle with a width of 5 centimeters and a length of 6 centimeters. If you draw another rectangle with a width of 6 centimeters and a length of 5 centimeters, are the two rectangles the same size and shape? Explain how you know.

MD-21.   Travis owns a blue van and a blue truck. Although he bought them both new, Travis has owned the truck for seventeen years longer than the van. If the sum of the ages of the vehicles is forty-one years, how old is the van and how old is the truck?

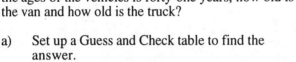

a)   Set up a Guess and Check table to find the answer.

b)   Show all your work and write your answer in a complete sentence.

MD-22.   What fraction of one hour (60 minutes) is represented by the following numbers of minutes? Simplify each fraction whenever possible. A sketch of a clock might help you.

a)   10 minutes   b)   15 minutes   c)   30 minutes   d)   20 minutes

MD-23.   Which of these answers is the correct simplification of $4 - (3 - 5)$?

(A) 12   (B) 6   (C) -2   (D) -4   (E) none of these

MD-24.   Mario used a pattern to write one-half many ways.

Example: $\frac{1}{2} = \frac{2}{4} = \frac{3}{6} = \frac{4}{8} = \frac{?}{?}$

a)   Study Mario's list. Write at least three more fractions equivalent to $\frac{1}{2}$.

b)   Marisa started a list of fractions equivalent to $\frac{1}{4}$: $\frac{1}{4} = \frac{2}{8} = ? = ? = ?$
     Add five more equivalent fractions to Marisa's list.

c)   Make a list of five fractions equivalent to $\frac{1}{3}$.

d)   Make a list of five fractions equivalent to $\frac{4}{4}$.

MD-25.   List three equivalent fractions for each fraction below.

a) $\frac{24}{36}$ b) $\frac{16}{20}$

MD-26.   Read the story of the Giant **1**, then complete the assignment that follows it.

Narrator: *Marisa understood Mario's pattern
            method for finding equivalent fractions
            pretty well. She thought she saw an easy
            way to create them.*

Marisa: Hey, Mario! Come here for a minute. I
            think I see something interesting about
            your pattern method.

Narrator: *Her brother, Mario, who was not thrilled
            about Marisa's discovery, grudgingly
            agreed to listen to her.*

Mario: Okay, okay. What do you see?

Narrator: *Marisa pointed to the example she had written on her paper.*

Marisa: Look at this! $\frac{4}{20}$ is the same as $\frac{1}{5}$, because I just multiplied the numerator of 1
            by 4 to get 4.

Mario: Okay, I'm with you so far.

Marisa: Next, I multiplied the denominator of $\frac{4}{5}$—5—by 4 and got 20. 4 over 4 is the
            same as 1.

>>Problem continues on the next page.>>

Narrator: *Mario understood Marisa's method, exclaiming,*

Mario: You're right. It is one, because four divided by four is one.

Narrator: *Mario excitedly summarized Marisa's method.*

Mario: So are you saying that when you multiply the numerator and denominator by the same number, you are really multiplying the whole fraction by 1?

Marisa: You've got it, Mario. A number multiplied by 1 is always the same number, that is, an equivalent number!

Mario: You're right, Sis! What should we call this method of finding equivalent fractions?

Narrator: *Marisa pondered for a moment.*

Marisa: I know. Let's call this method "multiplying by the Giant **1**!"

Narrator: *Mario considered Marisa's idea for a moment.*

Mario: I like that, Marisa! The Giant **1** it is! Let's try some problems.

The Giant **1** wears many disguises. What form does the Giant **1** take in each problem below?

a) $\frac{1}{3} \cdot \boxed{1} = \frac{4}{12}$ b) $\frac{3}{5} \cdot \boxed{1} = \frac{6}{10}$

c) $\frac{10}{15} = \frac{2}{3} \cdot \boxed{1}$ d) $\frac{5}{25} = \frac{1}{5} \cdot \boxed{1}$

MD-27.   When Marisa was multiplying by the Giant **1** to find equivalent fractions, she was actually using the **Identity Property of Multiplication**. The Giant **1** she used was in disguise as $\frac{4}{4}$. When she multiplied $\frac{1}{5}$ by $\frac{4}{4}$, she renamed the fraction $\frac{4}{20}$.

$$\frac{1}{5} \cdot \boxed{\frac{4}{4}} = \frac{4}{20}$$

Notice that $\frac{4}{20}$ and the original $\frac{1}{5}$ are just different names for the same number.

When multiplying by $\frac{4}{4}$, Marisa did not change the value of $\frac{1}{5}$. She just changed its name.

We can call Marisa's method the "Giant **1**" to remind us that when we multiply by the fractional forms of one (1) we are actually using the Identity Property of Multiplication.

>>Problem continues on the next page.>>

CHAPTER 3

Practice using the Identity Property of Multiplication (the Giant **1**) with these problems. Write the fraction you used for the Giant **1** each time.

a) $\frac{1}{3} \cdot \boxed{1} = \frac{3}{9}$

b) $\frac{3}{5} \cdot \boxed{1} = \frac{18}{30}$

c) $\frac{5}{8} \cdot \boxed{1} = \frac{40}{64}$

d) $\frac{20}{45} = \frac{4}{9} \cdot \boxed{1}$

e) $\frac{70}{110} = \frac{7}{11} \cdot \boxed{1}$

f) $\frac{6}{20} = \frac{3}{10} \cdot \boxed{1}$

MD-28.

IDENTITY PROPERTY OF MULTIPLICATION

FINDING EQUIVALENT FRACTIONS

Any number multiplied by one (1) equals itself. This is the **IDENTITY PROPERTY OF MULTIPLICATION**. That is, for any number n,

$$n \cdot 1 = n$$

This property is used to make **EQUIVALENT FRACTIONS**, that is, fractions that are equal but are written in <u>different</u> <u>forms</u>.

In general, $\frac{a}{b} \cdot \frac{c}{c} = \frac{ac}{bc}$. For example: $\frac{2}{3} \cdot \frac{4}{4} = \frac{(2)(4)}{(3)(4)} = \frac{8}{12}$.

Make these notes in your Tool Kit to the right of the double-lined box.

Write another example using the Identity Property of Multiplication to rewrite the fraction $\frac{3}{5}$.

MD-29. The electricity was out, and Mario was called to go out on an undercover mission. He had to grab some pants and a shirt from his closet in the dark. At that time there were five pairs of pants (2 jeans, 1 khaki, 2 black) and four shirts (2 gray, 1 white, 1 black) in his closet.

Draw a rectangle to organize the combinations in Mario's closet and to help you determine the following probabilities.

a) What is the probability that Mario chooses a pair of jeans and a black shirt?

>>Problem continues on the next page.>>

b) What is the probability that Mario chooses khaki pants and a white shirt?

c) Mario was hoping to get the black shirt and black pants for his midnight mission. What is the probability of that?

d) What is the probability Mario chooses black pants and a black shirt <u>or</u> jeans and a white shirt?

e) What is the most likely combination?

f) Rewrite the answers in parts (a), (b), and (c) as percents.

MD-30. What is the probability of Mario choosing a black shirt two days in a row?

MD-31. Write the first eight terms of a pattern based on $\frac{2}{3}$. Predict the 25th term of this pattern.

MD-32. Copy the problems below and use the Identity Property of Multiplication to complete the Giant **1** and replace the variable with the correct number.

a)

$$\frac{11}{22} = \boxed{\frac{11}{11}} \cdot \frac{y}{2}$$

b)

$$\frac{x}{4} \cdot \boxed{\frac{6}{6}} = \frac{6}{24}$$

c)

$$\frac{2}{3} \cdot \boxed{\frac{9}{9}} = \frac{18}{t}$$

d)

$$\frac{64}{96} = \boxed{1} \cdot \frac{8}{n}$$

e)

$$\frac{3}{6} \cdot \boxed{1} = \frac{21}{w}$$

f)

$$\frac{2}{8} \cdot \boxed{1} = \frac{12}{z}$$

MD-33. Marisa wondered if she could draw a model to understand equivalent fractions, such as $\frac{2}{3} = \frac{4}{6}$.

First, she drew a rectangle.

Then she divided the rectangle into thirds and shaded two of the thirds.

Next she divided the same rectangle into sixths and noticed that four-sixths were shaded. She could see that $\frac{2}{3} = \frac{4}{6}$ because the shaded areas were equal.

Draw models for parts (a) through (d) to represent each equivalent pair of fractions and, in part (d), replace the variable with the correct number.

a) $\frac{1}{4}$ and $\frac{2}{8}$

b) $\frac{6}{10}$ and $\frac{3}{5}$

c) $\frac{3}{4}$ and $\frac{9}{12}$

d) $\frac{4}{5}$ and $\frac{x}{10}$

MD-34. The girls' basketball team weighed the players. Their weights were 120, 122, 126, 130, 133, 147, 115, 106, 120, 112, and 142.

a)   Make a stem-and-leaf plot of their weights.

b)   What was the median weight?

c)   What was the range?

d)   What were the mean and mode?

MD-35. Marisa wanted to investigate some patterns. She wrote out some of them for you to complete.

a)   16, 8, 4, 2, 1, $\frac{1}{2}$, ___ , ___ , ___

b)   27, 9, 3, 1, ___ , ___ , ___

c)   16, 4, 1, ___ , ___ , ___

d)   Explain the pattern for part (b) in everyday words using complete sentences.

MD-36. The dotted line through the triangle at right is a **line of symmetry**. A line of symmetry means that the line divides the object into two halves which are mirror images of each other. How many lines of symmetry are on the rectangle? Sketch the rectangle and draw all the lines of symmetry you identified.

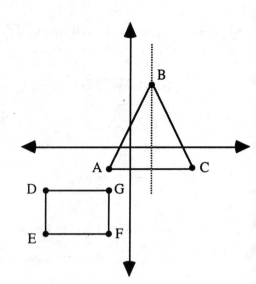

MD-37. Starting with $\frac{24}{60}$, work backward until the fraction is in its simplest form.

MD-38. If a pattern is based on $\frac{4}{9}$, what is the fifth term? What is the tenth term?

MD-39. What number divided by -3 gives 12 as the result?

(A) -36   (B) -4   (C) 4   (D) 36   (E) none of these

MD-40. Rectangles can be used to show multiplication of fractions. Draw a rectangle. Use one side of the rectangle to shade one of the fractions. Use the top or bottom to shade the other fraction. The overlapping shading is the product.

Example: $\frac{2}{3} \cdot \frac{1}{4}$

$= \frac{2}{12}$ or $\frac{1}{6}$

Draw a rectangle showing $\frac{1}{5} \cdot \frac{3}{4}$.

MD-41.	Match the multiplication problem with its correct generic model. Notice that the overlapping area represents the answer.

1. 	2.	3.	4.

a)　　$\frac{1}{4} \cdot \frac{3}{4}$　　　　　b)　$\frac{1}{2} \cdot \frac{1}{2}$　　　　c)　$\frac{1}{2} \cdot \frac{1}{3}$　　　　d)　$\frac{3}{5} \cdot \frac{2}{3}$

MD-42.	Draw a model for each of the following multiplication problems and write the answer.

a)　　$\frac{1}{4} \cdot \frac{1}{3}$　　　　　　　　　　b)　　$\frac{3}{4} \cdot \frac{1}{2}$

c)　　$\frac{1}{4} \cdot \frac{1}{5}$　　　　　　　　　　d)　　$\frac{3}{3} \cdot \frac{1}{2}$

MD-43. You will be playing the "Four-in-a-Row, There You Go" (Fraction Product) game, which is described below.

Four-in-a-Row, There You Go
A game for 2 to 4 people.

Mathematical Purpose: To practice fraction concepts.

Object: To cover four squares in a row, in a column, or diagonally; or, to cover the entire game board.

Materials: Game board, 2 paper clips

Scoring: One point for each "four in a row."

How to Play the Game:
- Use a fair method to decide who goes first.
- Player 1 (or Team 1) puts a paper clip on the long, narrow rectangular strip on the bottom of the game board so that it covers the fraction in the first small rectangle (usually $\frac{1}{2}$). The same player then places a second paper clip on another fraction along the bottom rectangle. Player 1 multiplies the two fractions and marks that product on the game board with an X.
- Player 2 may now move one (and only one) of the paper clips to another fraction along the bottom rectangle strip, then multiply and mark an O on the product of the two fractions on the game board.
- Players 1 and 2 take turns, each moving only one paper clip each turn and marking the product of the two fractions on the game board, until one side wins.
- Note: Not all possible answers are listed. If you choose $\frac{2}{3} \cdot \frac{1}{3} = \frac{2}{9}$ you lose a turn.

Ending the Game: The first person to get four squares in a row wins an individual game.

GAME BOARD

$\frac{1}{3}$	$\frac{8}{15}$	$\frac{1}{4}$	$\frac{3}{8}$
$\frac{2}{5}$	$\frac{3}{5}$	$\frac{3}{10}$	$\frac{1}{5}$
$\frac{1}{12}$	$\frac{1}{6}$	$\frac{2}{5}$	$\frac{1}{8}$
$\frac{4}{15}$	$\frac{12}{25}$	$\frac{1}{2}$	$\frac{3}{16}$

$\frac{1}{2}$	$\frac{2}{3}$	$\frac{3}{5}$	$\frac{1}{4}$	$\frac{3}{4}$	$\frac{1}{3}$	$\frac{4}{5}$

Your teacher will instruct you to play the game with your partner or as a class activity. When this has been completed, write "Game played" on your paper to let your teacher know you have done this activity. Include how many times you played and who won.

MD-44. These questions relate to the "Four-in-a-Row, There You Go" (Fraction Product) game.

a) Did you multiply the fractions by drawing out the diagram or did you use another strategy? If you used another strategy, describe it briefly

b) Explain why you chose your strategy.

MD-45. Look at the pair of spinners shown at right.

Spinner 1   Spinner 2

When Marisa and Mario went into Director Franklin's office, they were told that the choices for vehicles were two sedans and one truck. The colors were purple or green.

S-sedan   P-purple
T-truck   G-green

a) Sketch a probability table for this situation.

b) What is the probability of spinning a purple sedan (PS)?

c) Since $\frac{2}{3}$ of Spinner 1 is sedans and $\frac{1}{2}$ of Spinner 2 is purple, write a multiplication problem to describe the probability of spinning a purple sedan.

d) Write a problem to describe the probability of spinning a purple vehicle.

e) What is the probability of <u>not</u> spinning a green truck?

MD-46.

MULTIPLICATION OF FRACTIONS

To multiply fractions, multiply the numerators to make the new numerator and multiply the denominators to make the new denominator. Use the Identity Property (find any Giant **1**s in the product) to simplify the resulting fraction.

In general, $\frac{a}{b} \cdot \frac{c}{d} = \frac{ac}{bd}$.   Examples: $\frac{2}{3} \cdot \frac{1}{5} = \frac{2}{15}$

$\frac{3}{4} \cdot \frac{2}{3} = \frac{6}{12} = \frac{6}{6} \cdot \frac{1}{2} = \frac{1}{2}$

Write these notes in your Tool Kit next to the double-lined box.

a) In your own words, explain how to multiply fractions.

b) Explain how to simplify (reduce) a fraction.

MD-47.   Copy and complete the following multiplication table or use the resource page.

×	8	4	2	$\frac{1}{2}$	$\frac{1}{3}$	0
3						
6						
9						
$\frac{1}{2}$						
$\frac{1}{3}$						
$\frac{1}{4}$						

MD-48.   Use any of the strategies you have learned to find the unknown number in each problem below. Show all work.

a) $\dfrac{5}{9} = \dfrac{r}{27}$

b) $\dfrac{21}{28} = \dfrac{3}{k}$

c) $\dfrac{2}{3} \cdot \dfrac{6}{7} = x$

d) $\dfrac{3}{8} \cdot \dfrac{4}{5} = y$

e) $\dfrac{m}{12} = \dfrac{1}{4}$

f) $\dfrac{?}{?} \cdot \dfrac{3}{8} = \dfrac{12}{32}$

g) $\dfrac{c}{12} = \dfrac{3}{4}$

h) $\dfrac{3}{5} \cdot \dfrac{5}{3} = z$

MD-49   Judy likes to have a pen and a pencil when she takes notes or does classwork. Her special box contains 1 red, 1 blue, and 2 green pens. Judy also has 1 pink and 2 yellow pencils in the box. She likes to select her pen and pencil randomly. She is especially pleased when she pulls out a green pen and a pink pencil on testing days. Judy thinks this combination brings her good luck. Use the rectangle below to help you answer the questions.

a)   What is the probability that Judy pulls out a red pen and a yellow pencil?

b)   What is the probability that Judy pulls out a blue pen and a pink pencil?

c)   What is the probability that Judy pulls out a green pen and a yellow pencil?

d)   What is the probability that Judy pulls out a blue pen and a blue pencil?

e)   Today is a test day in Judy's class. What is the probability that she pulls out her "lucky" combination?

MD-50.   In her pencil box at home, Judy has four times as many pencils as pens. If she has seventy-five pens and pencils in her pencil box, how many does she have of each? Solve using a Guess and Check table.

MD-51.   Which choice(s) below can you quickly identify as incorrect answers for the product of 376 and 48?

(A) 4,243   (B) 18,048   (C) 18,480   (D) 18,038   (E) none of these

MD-52.   Follow your teacher's directions for practicing mental math. There are several ways to do the problem. Which method do you think is best?

MD-53.   Assuming each rectangle represents one whole unit, determine the total area of the shaded regions in parts (a) and (b) below.

a)   b)

MD-54.   In another pencil box, Judy has six pencils, eight markers, and three highlighters. As a shortcut we will use variables to write this as 6p + 8m + 3h. Her mom takes her to the store for more school supplies, and she comes home with a box of twelve pencils, a package of four highlighters, and one marker. If she adds the new supplies to her pencil box, how many of each type of writing utensil does she have now? Use variables to represent each type of item. Show your answer as an equation.

MD-55. Today we will look at just one spinner. What is the probability of spinning and getting a sedan or a motorcycle?

Since sedans are represented by $\frac{1}{3}$ of the area of the spinner and motorcycles are represented by $\frac{1}{4}$ of the area of the spinner, the probability of selecting either the sedan or the motorcycle is the sum of the two areas: $\frac{1}{3} + \frac{1}{4}$.

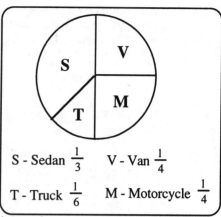

S - Sedan $\frac{1}{3}$ V - Van $\frac{1}{4}$

T - Truck $\frac{1}{6}$ M - Motorcycle $\frac{1}{4}$

This problem can be modeled using rectangles. Since the rectangles have fraction pieces of different sizes, both rectangles need to be divided into pieces that are the same size. If you visualize placing one rectangle on top of the other (while ignoring the shading for the moment), you can see the size of the pieces you need. In the example below, if you place the rectangle at right on top of the one at left, the horizontal and vertical lines create the rectangles below them. To find the sum of the fractions, write the total number of shaded pieces in relation to one rectangle.

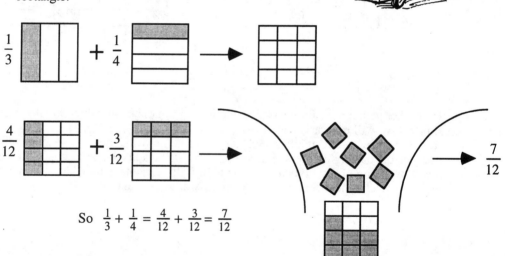

So $\frac{1}{3} + \frac{1}{4} = \frac{4}{12} + \frac{3}{12} = \frac{7}{12}$

Show how to add the following fractions using a three-step area model like the one above.

a) $\frac{2}{3} + \frac{1}{4}$ b) $\frac{1}{3} + \frac{1}{5}$

CHAPTER 3

MD-56. Marisa had to miss math class to go to the dentist, so she asked Mario to explain how to add fractions. He showed her this model.

$\frac{1}{3} + \frac{1}{2}$

"First you copy the problem.

"Next draw and divide equal-sized rectangles for each fraction. Remember that one is cut horizontally and the other is cut vertically.

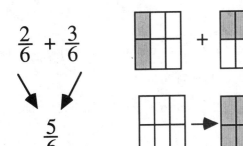

$\frac{2}{6} + \frac{3}{6}$

$\frac{5}{6}$

"Now redraw the rectangles with more lines, as if one rectangle is placed on top of the other one. Then shade the same areas from each of the two original rectangles.

"Now you can rename the fractions as sixths, because the new rectangles are divided into six equal parts. I drew an empty rectangle with sixths.

"Finally, combine all the sixths and shade the total number of sixths in the new rectangle. Then write one fraction."

Use the fraction model Mario explained to add the following fractions.

a) $\frac{1}{4} + \frac{2}{5}$

b) $\frac{2}{3} + \frac{3}{5}$

MD-57. Now we can find the probability of selecting a truck or van (parts (a) through (c)) and a sedan or van (parts (d) through (f)) using the spinner in problem MD-55.

a) Write a fraction addition problem to show the probability of spinning a truck or van.

b) Draw a rectangle model of your addition problem.

c) Find the sum using your model.

d) Write a fraction addition problem to show the probability of spinning a sedan or van.

e) Draw a rectangle model for your addition problem.

f) Find the sum using your model.

MD-58.   Skye's Ice Cream Shoppe is Mario's favorite place
for an outing. Unfortunately, because he was late
arriving there, his friends had already ordered. He
did not know what they ordered for him. They told
him that it was either a waffle cone or a sundae and
that it was either apricot, chocolate, or blackberry.

Draw, divide, and label a rectangle to answer the
following questions.

a)   What is the probability that Mario will get something with apricot ice cream?

b)   What is the probability that he will get a sundae?

c)   What is the probability that he will get either something with chocolate or a waffle
cone with blackberry?

d)   What is the probability that he will get orange sherbet?

MD-59.   Marisa and Mario were visiting the animals at the fair when they noticed a few number
relationships. They made them into brain teasers for you.

a)   If one-half of the pigs had spots and there
were 14 pigs, how many had spots?

b)   If three-fourths of the cows had nose rings
and there were 24 cows, how many cows
had nose rings?

c)   If three-tenths of the visitors were adults
and there were 100 visitors, what number
were adults?

d)   Five-eighths of the birds were chickens. If there were 64 birds, how many were <u>not</u>
chickens?

MD-60.   Calculate the sum or difference. Simplify when possible.

a) $\frac{1}{7} + \frac{3}{7}$ 　　　 b) $\frac{3}{8} + \frac{5}{8}$ 　　　 c) $\frac{2}{6} + \frac{2}{6}$ 　　　 d) $\frac{5}{6} + \frac{4}{6}$

e) $\frac{3}{4} + \frac{3}{4}$ 　　　 f) $\frac{5}{8} - \frac{3}{8}$ 　　　 g) $\frac{5}{10} - \frac{2}{10}$ 　　　 h) $\frac{1}{4} - \frac{3}{4}$

MD-61. Crystal and Cristina counted the number of letters in the last names of the students in their 7th period math class. Here is a list of their results: 9, 8, 4, 8, 7, 6, 5, 9, 7, 5, 6, 9, 8, 6, 6, 7, 7, 4, 6, and 6.

a) What is the mean number of letters?

b) What is the mode?

c) What is the range?

d) What numbers are in the upper quartile?

e) If Crystal's last name has 7 letters, in which quartile did her name fall?

f) What is the median number?

MD-62. Use the < and > symbols to complete the following inequalities.

a) -5 __ -2   b) 8 __ -1   c) -5 __ 0   d) -15 __ -14

MD-63. Which number represents the product of 731 and 640?

(A) 468,840   (B) 1,371   (C) 46,784   (D) 467,840   (E) none of these

MD-64. Complete the following Diamond Problems.

Product

Sum

a)

b)

c)

d) Bonus

MD-65. Judy has a pencil box on her desk with four blue, three red, and five yellow pencils. Her box also contains two red, one black, and three green pens. Whenever she reaches her hand in to get ready to do her homework, she randomly takes out one pencil and one pen.

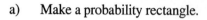

a)   Make a probability rectangle.

b)   How many pencils does Judy have in her box?

c)   How many pens does Judy have in her box?

d)   What is the probability that Judy gets a blue pencil?

e)   What is the probability that Judy gets a yellow pencil?

f)   What is the probability that Judy gets a green pen?

g)   What is the probability that Judy gets a black pen?

h)   What is the probability that Judy gets a blue pencil and a green pen?

i)   What is the probability that Judy gets a blue pencil and a red pen?

j)   What is the probability that Judy gets a blue pencil or a red pen?

MD-66.   Show how to add the following fractions using an area model.

a) $\frac{2}{3} + \frac{1}{5}$ b) $\frac{1}{4} + \frac{1}{6}$ c) $\frac{1}{3} + \frac{3}{8}$

MD-67.   You will be playing the "Four-in-a-Row, There You Go" (Fraction Addition) game. Make sure you use the new game board. You may want to review the rules in problem MD-43. In this game, however, instead of multiplying the two numbers, you add them. Also remember that some answers formed are not on the game board. When this game is completed, write "game played" on your paper to let your teacher know you have done this activity. Include how many times you played and who won.

GAME BOARD

$\frac{5}{6}$	$\frac{9}{10}$	$\frac{31}{40}$	$\frac{3}{4}$
$\frac{5}{8}$	$\frac{7}{8}$	$\frac{5}{12}$	$\frac{13}{24}$
$\frac{2}{3}$	$\frac{17}{30}$	$\frac{3}{8}$	$\frac{13}{20}$
$\frac{1}{2}$	$\frac{17}{24}$	$\frac{7}{24}$	$\frac{7}{12}$

$\frac{1}{2}$	$\frac{3}{8}$	$\frac{1}{6}$	$\frac{1}{4}$	$\frac{1}{8}$	$\frac{1}{3}$	$\frac{2}{5}$

ADDING AND SUBTRACTING FRACTIONS

To add or subtract two fractions, the fractions must have the same denominator. One way to convert two fractions with different denominators into fractions with the same denominator is to use a Giant **1**. Below are examples of adding and subtracting two fractions with unlike denominators. In general,

$$\frac{a}{b} + \frac{c}{d} = \frac{a}{b} \cdot \boxed{\frac{d}{d}} + \frac{c}{d} \cdot \boxed{\frac{b}{b}} = \frac{ad}{bd} + \frac{bc}{bd} = \frac{ad + bc}{bd}$$

ADDITION

$$\frac{1}{5} + \frac{1}{3} = \frac{1}{5} \cdot \boxed{\frac{3}{3}} + \frac{1}{3} \cdot \boxed{\frac{5}{5}} = \frac{3}{15} + \frac{5}{15} = \frac{8}{15}$$

SUBTRACTION

$$\frac{3}{4} - \frac{1}{5} = \frac{3}{4} \cdot \boxed{\frac{5}{5}} - \frac{1}{5} \cdot \boxed{\frac{4}{4}} = \frac{15}{20} - \frac{4}{20} = \frac{11}{20}$$

Answer the questions below in your Tool Kit to the right of the double-lined box.

a) What common denominator is needed to compute $\frac{1}{8} + \frac{2}{3}$?

b) Compute $\frac{1}{8} + \frac{2}{3}$ using the Giant **1**. Highlight the Giant **1**s you use.

MD-69. Using the spinner in problem MD-55, answer the following questions.

a) What is the probability of spinning either a truck or a sedan?

b) What is the probability of spinning either a truck or a van?

c) What is the probability of spinning either a motorcycle or a sedan?

MD-70.   Vehicle prizes were dwindling at the prize
          commission car lot. There were only two
          sedans, three vans, and one motorcycle left.
          When a new shipment arrived, it contained
          twelve new vans, four new motorcycles, and
          twenty new sedans. How many vehicle prizes
          are now on the lot? Use variables to represent
          each type of item and show your answer as an
          equation.

MD-71.   Vicki used $\frac{2}{3}$ of a cup of milk and $\frac{1}{4}$ of a cup of
          orange juice in her new recipe for Orange
          Cappuccinos. What is the total amount of milk
          and orange juice combined in the drink?

MD-72.   Betsy had one-quarter of a dozen eggs. Her chicken laid another one-sixth of a dozen
          eggs. What fraction of a dozen eggs does Betsy have now if she has neither eaten nor
          broken any eggs?

MD-73.   Ruthie did a survey among her classmates
          comparing the time spent playing video games to
          the time spent studying. The scatter plot of her
          data is shown at right.

          a)   What correlation can you make from her
                data?

          b)   Use an ordered pair to identify the outlier.

MD-74.   Answer the following questions about common denominators.

          a)   If you were adding thirds and fourths, what denominator would you use?

          b)   If you were adding fifths and twelfths, what denominator would you use?

          c)   If you were adding eighths and sixths, what denominator would you use?

          d)   How do you decide which new denominator to use? Explain in a few sentences.

MD-75.   In 1991, Doug Danger jumped 251 feet on his motorcycle. Based on a classroom 30 feet long, estimate how many classroom lengths he could jump.

MD-76.   Draw a model to represent multiplying the following fractions and give the answer.

a) $\frac{1}{2} \cdot \frac{4}{5}$ b) $\frac{3}{4} \cdot \frac{2}{3}$

MD-77.   Mario found a bag of marbles. It contained five blue marbles, seven green marbles, one agate, and two steelies. What is the probability of reaching into the bag and pulling out a blue marble or a steelie? Write an equation.

MD-78.   If a certain number is to be represented by x, and x is given a value of 7, what would be the value of $\frac{x+2}{3}$?

(A) 4   (B) 7x + 2   (C) 3   (D) x + 7   (E) none of these

MD-79.   How many hours will it take a person to travel 200 miles at the rate of 40 miles an hour?

(A) 25 hours   (B) $\frac{1}{4}$ hour   (C) 5 hours   (D) 2 hours   (E) none of these

MD-80.   Your teacher will give you a card or two to place on a number line. When all the cards are in place, draw an identical number line on your paper. Note that the number line focuses on the values between 0 and 1. Make your line long enough—at least five inches long—to fit each of the values in the correct place.

a)   Record all the numbers as they are placed on the class number line.

b)   Explain why some of the numbers name the same point.

c)   Discuss the similarities and differences between the values in the three sets of cards.

MD-81. Mario is concerned. Agent Ajax teaches the T^2 (Technology Training) course. She requires her students to earn at least 80% on tests to pass. Unfortunately, Mario only scored 39 out of 50 on the last test. He is sure that is just a little bit too low.

a) Express Mario's score as a fraction.

b) Use the Identity Property to create a fraction with a denominator of 100 to show this test score.

c) Write this fraction as a percent. (Percent means "out of one hundred.")

MD-82. Agent Ajax is a wonderfully compassionate, yet firm, teacher. While she will not make an exception on her 80% passing rule, she will allow Mario to take another test to try to improve his score. This time Mario scores 21 out of 25. Use the Identity Property of Multiplication to find Mario's score on the second test using a denominator of 100. In other words, write his score as a percent.

MD-83. Marisa is in the Fundamentals of Fingerprinting course, and the instructor, Agent Amino, is even tougher than Agent Ajax. He requires an 85% score to pass. However, he will allow students to choose the higher of two scores on the final exam. Marisa scored 43 out of 50 on one version of the final and 84 out of 100 on the other. Which score should Marisa choose?

MD-84. Tom is buying new computers for his writing team. He can buy the first five at dealer cost. The other 15 will be purchased for an extra $50 each. The cost of the computers totals $11,750. Use a Guess and Check table to find how much each of the discounted computers cost.

MD-85.   Draw a line segment on your paper that is at least 5 inches long. Divide the number line into ten equal intervals. Label the first tick mark 0.72 and the last (eleventh) tick mark 0.73. This segment represents the portion of the number line between 0.72 and 0.73. Place each of the following decimals in the proper spot on your number line.

a)   0.729   b)   0.724   c)   0.7231   d)   0.72732

e)   Round each of the numbers to the nearest hundredth. Using complete sentences, explain your strategy for rounding each number.

MD-86.   Complete the table on the resource page your teacher gives you.

Fraction	Decimal	Percent
$\frac{3}{4}$		
	0.25	
		50%
	$.3\overline{3}$	
$\frac{6}{25}$		
		80%

Fraction	Decimal	Percent
	0.4	
$\frac{5}{4}$		
	0.05	
		47%
$\frac{3}{2}$		
	0.01	

MD-87.   Look at the graph below.

a)   Enter the ordered pairs in the table below. Three pairs are done for you.

x	0	1				5		x
y	-7	-4				8		

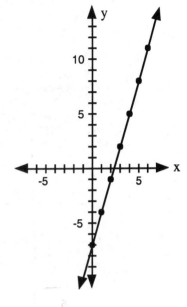

b)   Write the rule in two different ways: first using a variable and numbers, and then using words in a phrase or sentence.

c)   What are the coordinates of the y-intercept?

d)   What are the coordinates of the x-intercept? (You will have to approximate this point.)

MD-88.   Draw a square with sides of 5 units. What is the perimeter? What is the area? Be sure to label your answers.

MD-89.   Last week the low temperature in Fairbanks, Alaska was -6°. Which arrow is closest to -6° ?

A   B   C   D   E

–5   0   5

MD-90.   At one point in the last math competition, Marisa had 63 points. Then she answered a question incorrectly. The scorekeeper told her "-12 points." What was Marisa's score then?

(A) 75   (B) -12   (C) -75   (D) 12   (E) 51

MD-91.   Steve got 19 points out of 20 on his weekly quiz. Write this score as a:

a)   fraction   b)   decimal   c)   percent

MD-92.   Answer the following questions about common denominators.

    a)   If you were adding thirds and fifths, what denominator would you use?

    b)   If you were adding halves and sevenths, what denominator would you use?

    c)   If you were adding eighths and halves, what denominator would you use?

MD-93.   You will be playing "Four-in-a-Row, There You Go" (Fraction Subtraction). Make sure you use the new game board shown below. The rules are similar to problem MD-43 except that you will use subtraction. Again, not all possible answers are on the game board. Make sure you always subtract the smaller fraction from the larger fraction to get a positive result. When the game is completed, write "game played" on your paper to let your teacher know that you have done this activity. Include how many times you played and who won.

GAME BOARD

$\frac{1}{8}$	$\frac{1}{6}$	$\frac{9}{40}$	$\frac{7}{20}$
$\frac{1}{3}$	$\frac{1}{10}$	$\frac{1}{12}$	$\frac{4}{15}$
$\frac{1}{4}$	$\frac{5}{24}$	$\frac{13}{30}$	$\frac{1}{8}$
$\frac{3}{8}$	$\frac{3}{24}$	$\frac{1}{24}$	$\frac{1}{12}$

$\frac{1}{2}$	$\frac{3}{8}$	$\frac{1}{6}$	$\frac{1}{4}$	$\frac{1}{8}$	$\frac{1}{3}$	$\frac{2}{5}$

MD-94.   Mario decided to make some incomplete spinners to see if Marisa could figure out the missing piece.

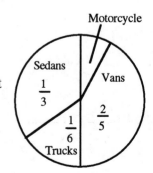

    a)   Marisa said, "This is easy. All I have to do is find out what to add to $\frac{2}{5}$ to get $\frac{1}{2}$." Write a problem that shows what she needs to do.

    b)   Solve the problem you wrote in part (a).

MD-95. Mario found a partially completed spinner that Director Franklin was making for the next day's class. He knew that if he put his problem-solving skills to use, he would be able to figure out the missing piece. Mario decided to break the problem into smaller problems (subproblems).

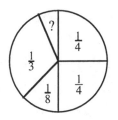

a) Describe the subproblems that Mario needs to solve to find the probability of getting the missing piece.

b) Solve the problem in part (a) above.

MD-96. Marisa thought that this was such a great activity that she wanted to make it more difficult and give it to someone else. She decided to add "convertibles" and change the probabilities. There is an equal chance of spinning either a van or a motorcycle. What is the probability of spinning a van? Show all of your subproblems.

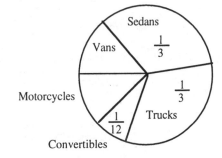

MD-97. Jonathan was baking bread one afternoon when the phone rang. While he was away from the kitchen, his dog Flexie came through and knocked some of the flour out of the measuring cup. Jonathan had a full cup when he left and only $\frac{3}{8}$ of a cup when he returned. How much did Flexie spill?

MD-98. Show the following values on a number line. Make the interval from 0 to 1 at least three inches long. Be as accurate as possible.

a) $\frac{5}{8}$

b) 0.307

c) 42.5%

d) 64%

e) $\frac{5}{6}$

f) 0.84

MD-99. Marisa and Mario ordered a large pizza dinner. When it arrived, Mario quickly ate $\frac{1}{8}$ of the pizza while Marisa answered the phone. When she called Mario to the phone, their pet poodle, Precious, jumped on the table and ate two large pieces that totaled $\frac{1}{3}$ of the pizza.

a) Draw a model of the pizza.

b) Write an equation to show the fraction of the pizza that was left.

c) About what percent of the pizza was left?

MD-100. Gale and Kaye are planning to make egg and bagel sandwiches for their group camping trip. They packed 30 eggs for breakfast. The first evening while they were out on a night hike, raccoons invaded the camp and ate some of the eggs. When the raccoons left, only $\frac{2}{5}$ of the eggs remained.

a) What fraction of the eggs did the raccoons eat?

b) How many eggs does this represent? Write an equation to show your work.

MD-101. Convert the following data and write equivalent measurements.

a) How many inches are there in 6 feet?

b) How many inches are there in 5 feet, 2 inches?

c) One hundred twenty-eight is how many times larger than 16?

d) One hundred twenty-eight is how many times larger than 8?

e) If Jon walked 16,412 feet, how many miles did he walk?

f) Ellen walked 85,764 inches. How many miles did she walk?

MD-102. Compute.

a)   -8 + (-3)

b)   4 – |-9|

c)   5 + (-7)

d)   8 + (-7)

e)   -2 – |-10|

f)   -9 – (-5)

g)   12 – 8

h)   (-3) · |-6|

i)   -3 + 6

j)   -20 ÷ 5

MD-103. Complete the following Diamond Problems.

Product

Sum

a)

b)

c)

d)

e)

MD-104. Use the resource page or copy and complete the tables below. Remember to show your work.

a)

A	B	A · B
3	4	3 · 4 = 12
-2	5	
-6	-3	
7	-2	
$\frac{1}{2}$	$\frac{1}{3}$	
$\frac{2}{5}$	$\frac{1}{3}$	

b)

A	B	$\frac{A}{B}$
6	3	$\frac{6}{3} = 2$
8	2	
1	2	
3	4	
2	7	
1	3	

MD-105. Look at your results from part (b) in the previous problem. Which fractions were easiest to convert to decimal form? Using complete sentences, explain why you think so.

MD-106. Marisa is back in the Fundamentals of
Fingerprinting course, and on the next exam Agent
Amino requires students to earn 83% to pass.
However, he will allow students to take two different
final exams and choose the higher of the two scores.
Marisa scored 81 out of 98 on one version of the
final and 85 out of 104 on the other.

a) Marisa is stuck. She cannot decide which
score to take. Mario suggests, "Fractions
mean division, right? Maybe we could just
divide 81 by 98 on our calculator and see what
decimal we get." Do this division, then write
the result.

b) Marisa continues, "0.826530612... is so weird! What percent is that? I know it
must be close to 82 or 83%, and I need to know which it is." What percent do you
think Marisa earned? Why do you think this?

c) "Oh, I think I can answer my own question. I know that percent means 'out of a
hundred,' so I'll round 0.826530612 to the nearest hundredth and write that as a
fraction." To what number does Marisa round 0.826530612...? What fraction
does she write?

d) Do parts (a), (b), and (c) for the other exam score.

e) "Oh wow!" exclaims Marisa. "Now it's obvious! I can just look at the fractions to
see which one is better. But wait, I need to know the two percents."

Mario counters with, "But if you know the decimals you already know the
percents."

Explain what Mario means.

f) Which score should Marisa choose?

MD-107. The following example shows Mario's reasoning. Mario started by noticing that
0.8173... is close to 0.82, which is just $\frac{82}{100}$. That's the secret. Remember: "Percent"
means "out of one hundred." So he knew that 0.82 meant 82%.
Convert the following decimals into percents or percents into decimals.

a) 0.48

b) 0.53

c) 0.76

d) 88%

e) 71%

f) 27.5%

MD-108. Make the conversions below. Show your work.

a) Change $\frac{5}{8}$ to a decimal.

b) Change 0.307 to a percent.

c) Change 42.5% to a decimal.

d) Change 64% to a fraction.

e) Change $\frac{5}{6}$ to a percent.

f) Change 0.84 to a fraction.

MD-109.

FRACTIONS—DECIMALS—PERCENTS

Fractions, decimals, and percents are different ways to represent the same number.

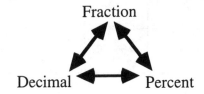

Examples:

Decimal to percent:

Multiply the decimal by 100.

(0.34)(100) = 34%

Percent to decimal:

Divide the percent by 100.

78.6% ÷ 100 = 0.786

Fraction to percent:

Set up an equivalent fraction using 100 as the denominator. The numerator is the percent.

$\frac{4}{5} = \frac{80}{100} = 80\%$

Percent to fraction:

Use 100 as the denominator. Use the percent as the numerator. Simplify as needed.

$22\% = 0.22 = \frac{22}{100} = \frac{11}{50}$

Decimal to fraction:

Use the decimal as the numerator. Use the decimal place value name as the denominator. Simplify as needed.

$0.2 = \frac{2}{10} = \frac{1}{5}$

Fraction to decimal:

Divide the numerator by the denominator.

$\frac{3}{8} = 3 \div 8 = 0.375$

In your Tool Kit, highlight the title (printed in italics) for each of the six ways to change the form of a number.

MD-110. Alexia's homework tonight is to design a spinner that will land on brown 35% of the time, pink 15% of the time, green 45% of the time, and purple the rest of the time.

    a)   What fraction of the spinner should Alexia color brown?

    b)   What fraction of the spinner should Alexia color pink?

    c)   What fraction of the spinner should Alexia color green?

    d)   What fraction of the spinner should Alexia color purple?

MD-111. Copy and complete the table.

$\frac{1}{6}$		
		≈ 66.7%
	0.42	
		15%
	0.357	
	0.0	
	1.0	
		200%

	1.6	
		37.5%
$\frac{1}{20}$		
		12.5%
$\frac{1}{10}$		
	0.001	
		24%
5		

MD-112. Which of the following bar graphs could represent the data from the circle graph?

    (A)   (B)   (C)   (D)   (E)

MD-113. Calculate the area and perimeter of the figure. Show all subproblems.

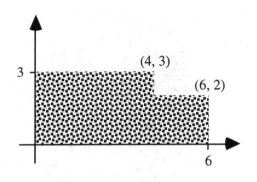

MD-114. Copy the scale at right and create a line graph for sales at the student store Monday through Friday. Notice that there are only four spaces on the vertical y-axis. You may use your Tool Kit as a model for how to set up interval(s). Put the day numbers on the horizontal x-axis. The data is shown below the graph. Remember to use your checklist to be sure your graph is complete.

Sales at the student store:
Day 1 $41.30
Day 2 $15.90
Day 3 $92.90
Day 4 $72.00
Day 5 $85.50

MD-115. Write approximate percents for the following fractions.

a) $\dfrac{25}{32}$

b) $\dfrac{17}{40}$

c) $\dfrac{75}{120}$

d) $\dfrac{36}{140}$

MD-116. Solve the following fraction problems.

a) $\dfrac{1}{3} + \dfrac{2}{5}$

b) $\dfrac{3}{4} \cdot \dfrac{2}{3}$

c) $\dfrac{5}{12} + \dfrac{1}{6}$

d) $\dfrac{3}{5} - \dfrac{1}{10}$

e) $\dfrac{3}{5} \cdot \dfrac{3}{10}$

f) $\dfrac{5}{24} + \dfrac{3}{12}$

MD-117.

Marisa ordered pizza. There were several choices of topping: pepperoni, artichokes, olives, tomatoes, and cheese. She knew the pizza baker, so she told him to surprise her. She also told him that she only wanted two toppings. What is the probability that she will get her favorite pizza, pepperoni with artichokes?

MD-118. In the fingerprinting course, Marisa and Mario took the same test. Mario's score was 12 points less than Marisa's score. The sum of their scores was 168. Using a Guess and Check table, find out what their scores were. Write your answer in a complete sentence.

MD-119. Your teacher will give you a resource page for the game you will be playing today.

Color-Combo-Grido II
A game for many people.

Mathematical Purpose: To study mathematical probability.

Object: To cover six squares in a row or to cover the entire game board.

Materials: 6 x 6 grid with squares divided in two parts; 2 dice each with three sides colored red, two sides colored green, and one side colored yellow.

Scoring: One point for a six-in-a-row game; five points for a cover game.

How to Play the Game:
- Label all 36 squares matching individual predictions.
- Caller rolls both dice and calls out colors.
- Mark out one square matching call (red/yellow and yellow/red are considered the same).
- Mark out only color combinations that match the call.
- Keep track of each play by tallying each color combination called.

Ending the Game: The first person with six in a row (horizontal, vertical, or diagonal) wins; or, the first person with his/her entire card marked out wins.

>>Problem continues on the next page.>>

CHAPTER 3

a) Discuss the game with your partner and make a prediction about what a winning card might look like.

b) Get a resource page from your teacher. Using methods learned in this chapter, analyze the color combination probabilities in the work area of your resource page. Then label your game board.

c) After the game is finished, copy the tally marks from the class game onto your resource page.

d) Compare each category that you originally put on your card to the probability found in your table.

e) Compare the class results to the probabilities you found with your probability rectangle.

f) Using complete sentences, compare the class results with the probabilities you found with your rectangle.

MD-120. The final exam in the National Investigative Agency contains a Color-Combo-Grido question. To pass the exam Mario and Marisa must analyze the situation and determine how often each combination is likely to occur.

Two dice are rolled. Each has sides colored red, red, red, green, green, and yellow.

a) When both dice are rolled, what color combinations are possible? Draw a probability rectangle, label the sides, and determine the probability of each possible combination. Give your answers as simplified fractions. Verify your answers before going on. Use these fractions to answer the following questions. Show all steps as you work.

b) Which color combination is most likely?

c) Which color combination is least likely?

d) What is the probability of getting either RR or RG?

e) What is the probability of both dice having the same color? Write an addition problem to find your answer.

MD-121. **Chapter Summary** Answer each of the following
questions to create a summary of this chapter.

a) Show how to find five fractions equivalent to $\frac{15}{24}$.

b) Write a clear explanation of how to add two
fractions so a student who just moved to your
school will understand. Use one of the sample
problems below or make up one of your own.
Use a rectangular area model and equations.

$\frac{1}{4} + \frac{3}{5}$ or $\frac{3}{7} + \frac{5}{9}$ or $\frac{5}{8} + \frac{1}{6}$ or $\frac{a}{b} + \frac{c}{d}$

c) The same new student does not understand multiplication of fractions. Explain wha
it means to multiply two fractions, such as $\frac{2}{3} \cdot \frac{4}{5}$. Use a picture and show the step
with numbers.

d) Select three different percents between 1% and 100% and show how to represent
them as decimals and as fractions. Choose problems more difficult than 25%, 50%
and 75%.

MD-122. There are 36 green gumballs, 18 red gumballs, 22 white
gumballs, 30 purple gumballs, and 14 blue gumballs in the
gumball machine. Find the probability for each of the
following situations and write it as a percent. Show work to
support your answer.

a) Getting a purple gumball.

b) Getting either a purple or a green gumball.

c) <u>Not</u> getting a green gumball.

d) Getting either a purple or a white gumball.

MD-123. Compute the answer to each problem.

a) $\frac{2}{7} + \frac{1}{3}$

b) $\frac{4}{5} + \frac{1}{3}$

c) $\frac{4}{9} + \frac{2}{3}$

d) $\frac{1}{4} \cdot \frac{3}{5}$

e) $\frac{4}{3} \cdot \frac{3}{4}$

f) $\frac{5}{7} - \frac{1}{3}$

MD-124. Harim has a bag with 3 blueberry and 4 raspberry gummy worms. He has another bag with 4 red licorice sticks and 2 black licorice sticks. Find the probabilities when he takes one gummy worm and one licorice stick out of each bag without looking.

a) Find the probability of Harim getting a blueberry gummy worm and a red licorice stick. Show your work. Express your answer in simplest form.

b) Find the probability of Harim getting a raspberry gummy worm and a black licorice stick. Show your work. Express your answer in simplest form.

c) Find the probability of Harim getting a blueberry gummy worm and a black licorice stick. Show your work. Express your answer in simplest form.

MD-125. Heidi has been busy with a painting project. She knows she can only spend eight hours on the project, and she estimates that she has already used two-thirds of her time. Write an equation to find how much time she has used. Make sure your answer is in hours and <u>minutes</u>.

MD-126. Calculate the following products. Write the problem, an equal sign, and the answer on your paper for each problem. (That is, write the equation with each solution.)

Note: whole numbers may be written as a fraction like this: $5 = \frac{5}{1}$.

a) $\frac{2}{3} \cdot 6$ b) $\frac{2}{5} \cdot 3$ c) $\frac{3}{4} \cdot 5$

MD-127. Barry took $\frac{1}{4}$ of $\frac{2}{3}$ of a cup of milk to make his special recipe. Write an equation to show how much he used. Show your work.

MD-128. **What We Have Done in This Chapter**

Below is a list of the Tool Kit entries from this chapter.

- MD-5   Probability
- MD-28   Finding Equivalent Fractions
- MD-46   Multiplication of Fractions
- MD-68   Adding and Subtracting Fractions
- MD-109   Fractions, Decimals, and Percents

Review all the entries and read the notes you made in your Tool Kit. Make a list of any questions, terms, or notes you do not understand. Ask your partner or study team members for help. If anything is still unclear, ask your teacher.

Going Camping

Chapter 4

Chapter 4
Going Camping: **ALGEBRAIC SENTENCES**

This chapter begins with a review of the order of operations. Next you will be introduced to the Distributive Property using a geometric model. Then you will use the patterns developed in Guess and Check tables to write equations with variables. Finally, algebra tiles will be used as a concrete model to help you understand simplifying algebraic expressions.

In this chapter you will have the opportunity to:

- write algebraic expressions and equations with variables.

- develop your understanding of the Distributive Property.

- evaluate algebraic expressions.

- combine like terms.

- review the order of operations by means of grouping terms.

Read the problem below, but **do not try to solve it now**. What you learn over the next few days wil enable you to solve it.

GC-0.	**Hannah's Trail Mix**

Hannah, the camp cook, uses a standard recipe for trail mix that contains raisins, chocolate pieces, and peanuts. The quantity of chocolate pieces is 4 ounces more than 3 times the number of ounces of raisins. The quantity of peanuts is 5 ounces less than twice the number of ounces of raisins. What quantity of each ingredient does Hannah use in her standard recipe? Use a variable to write an equation to represent the recipe.

Number Sense	
Algebra and Functions	
Mathematical Reasoning	
Measurement and Geometry	
Statistics, Data Analysis, & Probability	

Chapter 4
Going Camping: **ALGEBRAIC SENTENCES**

GC-1. Copy the Mess Hall Breakfast Menu expressions and evaluate them as your teacher gives them to you. For example, in the first entry, p + m, we let p represent the cost of pancakes and m represent the cost of milk. Likewise, the cost of each of the other items on the menu is represented by the first letter of its name. To evaluate an expression means to calculate the value.

GC-2. Evaluate each of the following expressions:

a) $6 + 5 \cdot 8$

b) $3 \cdot 5 + 2 \cdot 10$

c) $3 + 2(4 + 7)$

GC-3. Work with your partner to evaluate the problems below. Circle each term and show all your steps in the same way demonstrated by your teacher.

a) $17 + 3 \cdot 2$

b) $7 \cdot 2 + 4 - 2(7 + 3)$

c) $6 \cdot 2 + 3 \cdot 4 - 8$

d) $3^2 + 5(1 - 3) + 4 \cdot 5 + 1$
Remember that 3^2 means $3 \cdot 3$.

e) $(8 - 12) + 10 \cdot 3$

GC-4.   You will be playing the Target Game today. You will play this game throughout the chapter, and it will help you practice using the correct order of operations. Some homework problems will refer to the game.

Target Game
A game for the whole class

Mathematical Purpose: To practice the order of operations.

Object: Use any combination of the five numbers given and any combination of arithmetic operations to reach an answer that is as close as possible to the target number.

How to Play the Game:
- Your teacher will give you five numbers and a target number.
- Arrange the five numbers in any order and use any combination of mathematical operations and grouping symbols (addition, subtraction, multiplication, division, exponents, and parentheses) to write an equation that has an answer as close as possible to the target number.
- The winner is the person who gets closest to the target number.

Ending the Game: The game ends when the teacher determines that all students have had enough time to write their best equation.

GC-5.   Simplify each expression.

a) $16 - 5(3 - 1)$

b) $3(2^2) - 8 \cdot 1$

c) $4 \cdot 5 - 2^2 + 3(5 - 4)$

GC-6.

ORDER OF OPERATIONS

An expression is organized into parts that are separated by addition (+) or subtraction (−) symbols <u>unless</u> the sum or difference is inside parentheses. Each part (a number, variable, product or quotient of numbers and variables) is called a **TERM.**

1. <u>Circle</u> the terms in the expression.

2. <u>Simplify</u> each term until it is one number by:

   • evaluating each exponential number.

   • performing each operation inside prentheses before doing any other operations in the term following the rule below.

   • multiplying and dividing from left to right.

3. Finally, <u>combine like terms</u> by adding and subtracting left to right.

Example:

Simplify $3(6-3) + 4 \cdot 5^2 - 10$.

$$\boxed{3(6-3)} + \boxed{4 \cdot 5^2} - \boxed{10}$$

$$\boxed{3(3)} + \boxed{4 \cdot 5 \cdot 5} - \boxed{10}$$

$$\boxed{9} + \boxed{4 \cdot 25} - \boxed{10}$$

$$\boxed{9} + \boxed{100} - \boxed{10}$$

$$109 - 10 = 99$$

Examples of a term include 4, 3x, $-2y^4$, $\frac{3x}{7}$, 4(x + 3), and $5x(x - 2)^2$.

Make these notes in your Tool Kit to the right of the double-lined box.

a) Describe some mistakes students might make if they do not know the order of operations.

b) How will you help yourself remember the correct order of operations?

GC-7. Use the order of operations and a table like the one at right to calculate the y-values. Leave enough space on each line to show your work. Follow the example and show all your work. You do <u>not</u> need to copy the example onto your paper. Just draw two vertical and one horizontal lines to create the table workspace. Some of the answers are in your book, so you may want to use these answers to check your work and make sure you are doing the problems correctly.

x	y = 3x + 5	y
-2	y = 3(-2) + 5	
	$y = \boxed{3(-2)} + \boxed{5}$	
	$y = \boxed{-6} + \boxed{5}$	
	y = -1	-1
0		
2		
-1		2

GC-8. You have been given the numbers 2, 3, 4, 5, and 6 in the Target Game. The target that you are trying to get is 19. Someone has already found 20 and 18.

a) Find a winning solution. b) Find another solution.

c) Are there more solutions? Check with your partner or study team members to see whether they found other solutions.

GC-9. The camp soccer teams calculate their statistics each summer. Here are the statistics for the top six teams. Round your answers to the nearest tenth.

	Games Played	Games Won	Games Lost	Goals Scored
Burn	52	42	10	162
Sizzlers	27	20	7	74
100°	28	16	12	87
Hotdoggers	30	16	14	53
Flash	33	28	5	102
Coolers	48	37	11	139

a) Find the mean number of games played by all of the teams.

b) Find the number of goals per game scored by the Coolers.

c) Find the median number of games lost for all of the teams. Which teams are closest to the median?

d) Find the median number of games won. Which teams are closest to the median?

GC-10. Lani and Will are arguing about whether $\frac{3}{6}$ and $\frac{50}{100}$ are equivalent fractions. Will says they are and Lani says they are not because you cannot use the Identity Property of Multiplication to change $\frac{3}{6}$ to $\frac{50}{100}$. Who is correct? Explain your answer.

GC-11. Use the resource page provided by your teacher to make your own set of algebra tiles. Cut out the tiles and store them in the envelope provided by your teacher.

GC-12. Now that we have started a new chapter, it is time for you to organize your binder.

a) Put the work from the last chapter in order and keep it in a separate folder.

b) When this is completed, write, "I have organized my binder."

GC-13. Play the Target Game and aim for a target number of 40. Use 1, 3, 4, 4, and 7. Find two solutions.

GC-14. Compute answers to the following problems in your head. Write just the answers on your paper.

a) $13 \cdot 8$

b) $10 \cdot 8 + 3 \cdot 8$

c) $7 \cdot 15$

d) $7 \cdot 10 + 7 \cdot 5$

e) $4 \cdot 198$

f) $4 \cdot 200 - 4 \cdot 2$

g) Examine the expressions by pairs, that is, parts (a) and (b), (c) and (d), and (e) and (f).

i) How is each pair similar?

ii) How is each pair different?

h) Make up two more pairs of examples like the ones above.

GC-15. Follow the steps below to calculate the area of this rectangle.

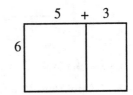

a) Find the area (in square units) of the two smaller rectangles.

b) Add the areas of the two sections.

c) Find the length of the big rectangle by adding the (horizontal) lengths of the two smaller rectangles.

d) Multiply the new length by the width.

e) What do you notice about your answers in parts (b) and (d)?

f) Write an equation to show that both methods give the same result.

GC-16.	Use the Distributive Property to break each problem into smaller parts, called **subproblems**, then multiply and add or subtract the products.

a)	$6 \cdot 31$	b)	$4 \cdot 37$	c)	$85 \cdot 7$	d)	$50 \cdot 28$

GC-17.	Use the Distributive Property to help make working with larger numbers simpler.

a)	Explain how you could break $4 \cdot 625$ into **subproblems** to make it easier to solve

b)	Write out your steps in the form of an equation.

c)	Compare your steps with another member of your team. Did you approach the problem in the same way or in different ways? Explain.

GC-18.

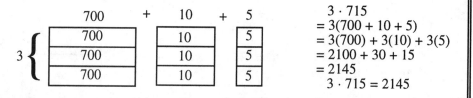

DISTRIBUTIVE PROPERTY WITH INTEGERS

- Rewrite the multiplication problem as two or more terms of products to be added or subtracted.
- Multiply the separate parts.
- Add or subtract the products.

Example 1: $6 \cdot 37 = 6(30 + 7) = 6 \cdot 30 + 6 \cdot 7 = 180 + 42 = 222$

Example 2: $3 \cdot 715$

$$3 \cdot 715$$
$$= 3(700 + 10 + 5)$$
$$= 3(700) + 3(10) + 3(5)$$
$$= 2100 + 30 + 15$$
$$= 2145$$
$$3 \cdot 715 = 2145$$

Answer the question in your Tool Kit to the right of the double-lined box.

How can the Distributive Property help you with the mental math problems you do in your head? Give an example.

GC-19.	Show all your subproblems and write your answer as an equation.

a)	$5 \cdot 320$	b)	$4 \cdot 408$	c)	$7 \cdot 906$

GC-20. Use the picture at right to help you multiply 12 · 17. Refer to problem GC-15 if you need help. Show all your subproblems.

	7 +	10
12	A	B

GC-21. Travis had $\frac{3}{8}$ of a box of crackers and Shellena had $\frac{7}{8}$ of a box. They need one and a half boxes for their party. Do they have enough? Explain your answer.

GC-22. When Edwin's class went to the School Fair the students guessed how many jelly beans were in a jar. Here are their guesses: 75, 80, 95, 92, 100, 72, 71, 60, 65, 88, 44, 78, 82, 83, 86, 102, 116, 101, 60.

a) Make a stem-and-leaf plot to display the data.

b) Make a box-and-whisker graph.

c) Which data display most clearly shows the range of the data? What is the range?

d) Which data display most clearly shows the mode? What is the mode?

GC-23. Use a table like the one at right and the order of operations to calculate the y-values. Follow the example and show all of your work for each y-value.

x	y = 5 + 3(2 − x)	y
-3	y = 5 + 3(2 − (-3))	
	y = ⑤ + ③(2 − (-3))	
	y = ⑤ + ③(5)	
	y = ⑤ + ⑮	
	y = 20	20
-2		17
2		
0		

GC-24. How was the Identity Property of Multiplication (the Giant **1**) used to find equivalent fractions for the problems below?

a) $\frac{2}{3} \cdot$ 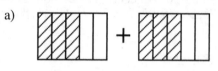 $= \frac{12}{18}$

b) $\frac{6}{7} \cdot$ $= \frac{48}{56}$

c) $\frac{49}{63} = \frac{7}{9} \cdot$ 1

d) $\frac{24}{27} = \frac{8}{9} \cdot$ 1

GC-25. Assuming each rectangle represents one whole unit, determine the total area of the shaded parts in the problems below.

a)

b)

GC-26. Follow your teacher's directions for practicing mental math. How are the new solution strategies helping you?

GC-27. Garret was playing the Target Game. The numbers rolled were 2, 3, 5, 6, and 7, and the target number was 31. Help Garret hit the target. Find two or three solutions and be ready to write one on the board.

GC-28. Holly Anne has a flower garden with two planting beds. She asked Chad and Scooter to help her find the total area of her garden. Here is what they did:

Chad's Method	Scooter's Method
$4(5 + 2)$	$(4 \cdot 5) + (4 \cdot 2)$
$= 4 \cdot 7$	$= 20 + 8$
$= 28$	$= 28$

a) Explain each step of Chad's method.

b) Explain each step of Scooter's method.

c) Which method do you prefer? Why?

GC-29.   Perform the following computations.

   a) $(6 \cdot 3) + (6 \cdot 9) + (6 \cdot 1) + (6 \cdot 7) = ?$ b) $6(3 + 9 + 1 + 7) = ?$

   c)   What is the same about each problem?   d)   What is different about the problems?

GC-30.   Carefully examine the rectangles at right.

   a)   What are the dimensions of Figure A?

   b)   Find the area of Figure A.

   c)   What are the dimensions of Figure B?

   d)   Find the area of Figure B.

   e)   Add the areas of Figures A and B.

   f)   What are the dimensions of Figure C?

   g)   Find the area of Figure C.

   h)   What do you notice about the combined areas of Figures A and B and the area of Figure C?

   i)   Draw a new diagram showing how Figures A and B could fit <u>inside</u> Figure C. Explain why this is possible.

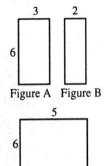

Figure A   Figure B

Figure C

GC-31.   Use a resource page or copy the table below, then use the Distributive Property to complete it.

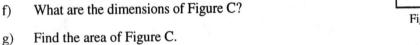

Factored Form	Distributed	Simplified
$3(7 + 2)$	$3(7) + 3(2)$	$21 + 6 = 27$
$8(7 + 4)$	$8 \cdot 7 + 8 \cdot 4$	
$9(4 + 3 + 1)$		
$2(7 + 5 + 6)$		
	$5 \cdot 8 + 5 \cdot 3 + 5 \cdot 9$	
$6(4 + 3 + 7 + 10)$		

GC-32.   Try each problem using mental math and write only your answer. Then write out steps that illustrate the Distributive Property.

   a) $731 \cdot 4$ b) $3 \cdot 256$ c) $625 \cdot 5$ d) $7 \cdot 514$

GC-33.   One number is five more than a second number. The product of the numbers is 2,444, and both numbers are positive. Use a Guess and Check table to find the numbers.

GC-34. The graph at right shows an
example of a translation
(slide). In the triangle,
A (-6, -1) moved to
A' (1, 2), etc.

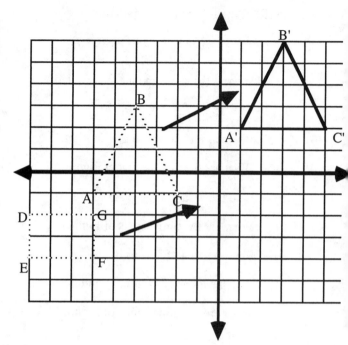

a) If B = (-4, 3) what are
the coordinates of B'?

b) If rectangle DEFG
slides in the same
manner as the triangle,
draw rectangle
D'E'F'G'.

c) What are the
coordinates of the
vertices of the
translated rectangle?

GC-35. Counselors want to paint all the cabins before the
campers arrive. They are going to work different
amounts of time. Chris will work five hours,
Caylan will work three, Cara will work two, Rachel
and Alyssa will each work four, and Levi will work
six hours. If each counselor earns $6 an hour, what
is the total amount the owner will have to pay to
have the cabins painted? Use the Distributive
Property to show how to solve this problem in two
ways by completing parts (a) and (b) below.

a) Calculate how much each counselor will earn and add their earnings together. Write
your answer in an equation.

b) Add all of the counselors' hours together first and then calculate the total earnings.
Write your answer in an equation.

GC-36. Convert these measurements. How many:

a) inches are in 27 feet?   b) centimeters are in 14 meters?

c) weeks are in 42 days?   d) pounds are in 32 ounces?

CHAPTER 4

GC-37. Draw a model for each of the following multiplication problems and give the answer.

a) $\frac{1}{2} \cdot \frac{1}{3}$ b) $\frac{2}{3} \cdot \frac{1}{4}$

c) $\frac{1}{5} \cdot \frac{2}{3}$ d) $\frac{4}{4} \cdot \frac{3}{4}$

GC-38. Below are three scatter plots. For each scatter plot, answer the following questions.

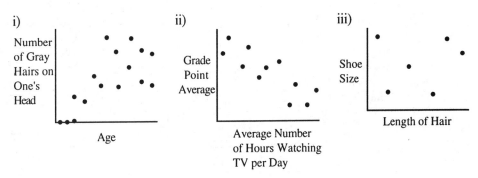

i) Number of Gray Hairs on One's Head — Age

ii) Grade Point Average — Average Number of Hours Watching TV per Day

iii) Shoe Size — Length of Hair

a) What does a dot on each scatter plot represent?

b) Is there a "trend" or correlation in the group of dots? If so, describe it.

c) Write positive correlation, negative correlation, or no correlation.

GC-39. Copy the Mess Hall Lunch and Dinner Menu expressions and evaluate them as your teacher gives them to you. Each variable represents the cost of the item with the same first letter in its name.

GC-40. You have made or been provided with a set of tiles in three different sizes. These are called algebra tiles. The big square has a side length of x, the narrow rectangle has sides of length 1 (the short side) and x (the long side), and the small square has a side length of 1.

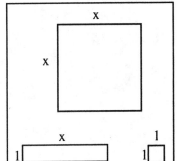

a) Trace and label the dimensions of each tile on your paper.

b) What is the area of the big square?

c) What is the area of the rectangle?

d) What is the area of the small square?

GC-41.   Remember that x can represent any number, just as the variable did in the envelope activity in Chapter 2. Remember that x has the same value <u>within</u> <u>each</u> <u>problem</u>, but its value can vary from problem to problem.

a)   Find the area of each tile in the previous problem when x = 5.

b)   Check your results with your team members. Did you agree or disagree? Explain.

c)   Why do you think x is called a **variable**?

GC-42.   Here is another example of combining like terms with a diagram. Use it as your model. Draw a diagram, then write an equation for (a) through (c) below.

$$(2x^2 + 5x + 7) + (x^2 + x + 1) = 3x^2 + 6x + 8$$

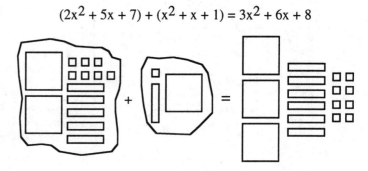

a) $(x^2 + 2x + 3) + (2x^2 + 5x + 4)$

b) $(3x^2 + 3x + 6) + (2x + 8)$

c) $(2x^2 + 10) + (6x + 2)$

GC-43.

HOW TO COMBINE LIKE TERMS

Group all of the tiles with the same area. Doing so models an algebraic process called **COMBINING LIKE TERMS**.

Note: The formal definition of **like terms** is two or more terms that have the same variable(s) with corresponding variable(s) raised to the same power.

Examples: 6 and 13, $2x^2$ and $-7x^2$, 4ab and 3ab.

<u>Not</u> like terms: 5 and 3x, 5x and $3x^2$, ab and ab^2.

List terms in order of decreasing powers.

Tile model:

$$(x^2 + 2x + 4) \quad + \quad (x^2 + x + 2) \quad = \quad 2x^2 \quad + \quad 3x \quad + \quad 6$$

Make these notes in your Tool Kit to the right of the double-lined box.

a) Here is a real-world example of combining like terms:

If you have 8 pens and 3 pencils and your friend has 1 pen and 7 pencils, together you have 9 pens and 10 pencils.

Give two more real-world examples of combining like terms.

b) Use mathematical numbers and symbols to give three examples of like terms. Have your partner or a team member check that your examples are correct.

GC-44. Nadine and Patricia put some of their algebra tiles together in a container on the desk. Nadine put in two big squares, three rectangles, and four small squares. Patricia added two rectangles and three small squares.

a) Draw a diagram that shows the tiles each girl put in the container.

b) Write an equation to describe what is now in the container. Your equation should look like this: (   ) + (   ) = _____.

GC-45.   You were busy working on a problem using four big squares, eight rectangles, and six small squares. Your partner accidentally knocked some algebra tiles off your desk. You now have one big square, three rectangles, and five small squares on your desk.

Write an algebraic equation that shows what tiles you began with, what your partner knocked off the desk, and how many tiles you have left.

GC-46.   Use the Distributive Property to add parentheses and write these expressions as a product a number and a sum. Expressions written like this are said to be in **factored form**. Here an example to use as a model: $6 \cdot 3 + 6 \cdot 7 = 6(3 + 7) = 6(10) = 60$.

a) $8 \cdot 3 + 8 \cdot 2$

b) $31 \cdot 4 + 31 \cdot 6$

c) $25 \cdot 8 + 25 \cdot 12$

d) $7 \cdot 131 + 7 \cdot 86$

GC-47.   Use the Identity Property of Multiplication (Giant 1) to figure out the unknown number.

a) $\frac{3}{7} = \frac{r}{28}$

b) $\frac{24}{36} = \frac{4}{k}$

c) $\frac{2}{3} = \frac{x}{33}$

d) $\frac{n}{8} = \frac{42}{56}$

e) $\frac{m}{64} = \frac{1}{8}$

f) $\frac{4}{5} \cdot \frac{?}{?} = \frac{36}{45}$

g) $\frac{c}{6} = \frac{48}{72}$

h) $\frac{3}{5} \cdot \frac{?}{?} = \frac{21}{35}$

GC-48.   Copy and complete the multiplication table. Put fractional answers in their simplest form.

Multiply	4	2	$\frac{1}{2}$	$\frac{1}{3}$	0
$\frac{1}{2}$					
$\frac{1}{3}$			$\frac{1}{6}$		
$\frac{1}{4}$					

GC-49. Ona went on a houseboat vacation. Her three-day rental rate was $745. She could keep the houseboat for any number of extra days for $150 per day over the three-day rate. When she returned the houseboat, her bill was $1495. Use a Guess and Check table to find how many extra days she stayed on the river.

GC-50. The camp cabins have two rooms. One room contains bunk beds and the other room is the bathroom.

Draw a diagram and find the total area of the cabin in two ways. Assume the cabin is rectangular and the sleeping area measures eight feet by ten feet. The bathroom is eight feet by four feet. Write an equation to show your work both ways.

GC-51. Complete the following fraction-decimal-percent triangles.

a)

$$\frac{4}{5}$$

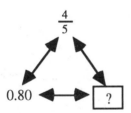

0.80 ⟷ [?]

b)

$$\frac{2}{5}$$

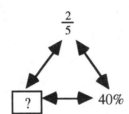

[?] ⟷ 40%

c)

[?]

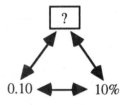

0.10 ⟷ 10%

GC-52. Use the order of operations and a table like the one at right to calculate the y-values. Follow the example given as a model. Show all of your work for each y-value.

x	y = 2x + 3(x + 1)	y
-2	y = 2(-2) + 3(-2 + 1) y = (2(-2)) + (3(-2 + 1)) y = (-4) + (3(-1)) y = (-4) + (-3) y = -7	-7
-1		
0		
3		

GC-53. Claire finished her assignment early, so her teacher suggested that she find the last digit of the product $3 \cdot 3^3 \cdot 3^5 \cdots 3^{19}$. The entire product was too big for her calculator, but she still found the last digit. What is the last digit? Explain how she determined her answer.

GC-54. Match each geometric figure with the algebraic expression that describes it. Note: "3 · x" means "3 times x" and is often written 3x. This represents 3 rows of length x. Sketch a quick copy of the figure and write the expression below it.

a)

b)

$2(x) + 2(1)$

$3(x + 1)$

c)

d)

$5(x + 2)$

$3(x) + 3(3)$

$2(x + 4)$

$3(x) + 3(5)$

e)

f)

GC-55. Sketch the geometric figure represented by each of the algebraic expressions.

a) $4(x + 3)$ b) $4(x) + 4(3)$

c)   Compare the diagrams. How do their areas compare? Write an algebraic equation that states this relationship. This is another example of the Distributive Property.

C-56.   Each algebraic expression below can be represented with algebra tiles in two different ways to show the Distributive Property. Use your algebra tiles to build two geometric figures for each expression. The first one has been done for you.

a)   3(x) + 3(2)

          Build 3(x) + 3(2).   Group them differently.

      3 rows of x and 3 rows of 2   3 rows of (x + 2)
              3(x) + 3(2)   =   3(x + 2)

b)   2(x + 8)   c)   4(x + 2)

d)   5(x) + 5(4)   e)   5(x + 6)

f)   9(x) + 9(4)   g)   2(4x + 7)

h)   6(x + 3)

C-57.

DISTRIBUTIVE PROPERTY WITH ALGEBRA TILES

Using the Distributive Property, the area of a rectangular arrangement of algebra tiles can be represented in three different ways.

        3x + 9   3(x) + 3(3)   3(x + 3)

        area = 3x + 9 = 3(x) + 3(3) = 3(x + 3)

        In general, ab + ac = a(b) + a(c) = a(b + c)

Make these notes in your Tool Kit to the right of the double-lined box.

a)   How is this Tool Kit entry different from the previous Tool Kit entry on the Distributive Property?

b)   How is it the same?

c)   How does the Distributive Property relate to area as a sum and area as a product?

C-58.   Your random numbers are 7, 2, 3, 9, and 5. Your target number is 52. Find two or three solutions that hit or come as close as possible to the target number. Show your work.

GC-59. Use the order of operations and a table like the one at right to calculate the y-values. Use the example given as a model. Show all of your work for each y-value.

x	y = 3(x + 6) – 2	y
-3	y = 3(-3 + 6) – 2 y = (3(-3 + 6)) – (2) y = (3(3)) – (2) y = (9) – (2) y = 7	7
-2		
-1		
0		

GC-60. What value of x makes each equation true?

a) x + 12 = 56   b) -10 + x = -32   c) x – 15 = 53   d) x + (-7) = 25

GC-61. Several campers want to paint a mural. The wall where the mural will be painted has been divided into three sections. The height is 8 feet, and the width of each section is different. One section measures 8 feet by 6 feet. Another section measures 8 feet by 4 feet. The third section measures 8 feet by 5 feet.

a)   Draw a diagram of the wall and label the dimensions of the three sections.

b)   Find the area of each section.

c)   Find the total area of the camp mural. Show your computation in two ways.

d)   Explain how using the Distributive Property relates to finding the area of the camp mural.

GC-62. Simplify the following.

a) $\frac{1}{2} + \frac{1}{3}$

b) $1\frac{1}{2} + 1\frac{1}{3}$

c) $\frac{1}{2} + \frac{2}{3}$

d) $1\frac{1}{2} + 1\frac{2}{3}$

GC-63. Use the Breakfast Mess Hall Menu below to help you solve these problems. Remember that we represent the cost of an item by using the first letter of its name. Copy the expressions and evaluate them.

MESS HALL MENU

BREAKFAST
Sausage	$1.75
Egg	$1.25
Hash Browns	$1.90
Pancakes	$1.75
Toast	$1.35
Donut	$1.50
Fruit	$2.50

BEVERAGES
Juice	$1.15
Milk	$0.75
Cocoa	$0.90

a) $3s + 2e + m$

b) $5f + j$

c) $2(h + t + p)$

d) $12d$

GC-64. Follow your teacher's directions for practicing mental math. Write down a strategy that you like best.

GC-65. Use the Lunch/Dinner Mess Hall Menu below to help you solve these problems. Remember that we represent the cost of an item by using the first letter of its name. Copy the expressions and evaluate.

MESS HALL MENU

LUNCH/DINNER
Hamburger	$1.95
Cheese Burger	$2.25
Veggie Burger	$2.50
Fries	$0.95
Green salad	$2.05
Pasta	$2.75
Taco	$3.50

BEVERAGES
Small	$1.05
Medium	$1.65
Large	$2.00
Extra Large	$2.35

a) Rasheed ordered a hamburger, fries, and a beverage, and he paid $5.25. Write an equation to represent this situation. Replace the variables for the hamburger and fries with their prices and determine the size of the beverage he ordered. Use b to represent the cost of a beverage.

>>Problem continues on the next page.>>

b) Three of his friends asked him to order each of them a cheeseburger, fries, and the largest possible beverage they could get while keeping the price under $5 apiece. Write an expression representing the new order. Use b as a variable to represent the cost of the beverage. Write this expression in two ways.

c) Find the value of b in the expression you wrote in part (b).

d) What size beverage did he order for each friend?

GC-66. Yolanda was playing a new Target Game called Integer Target Game. The integers she us were 9, -3, 8, -1, and 5. Her target was 58. How close can you come to Yolanda's targe

GC-67. Use a resource page or copy and fill in the table below using the Distributive Property.

Factored Form	Distributed	Simplified
4(x + 7)	4(x) + 4(7)	4x + 28
9(x – 1)		
2(x + 9)		
6(x + y)		6x + 6y
3(2x – 5)		
	4(y) – 4(3)	4y – 12
10(x + y)		

GC-68. The camp nurse reported 38 cases of poison oak during the first two days at camp. On the second day there were 16 more cases than the first. How many cases were there the first day? How many cases were there the second day? Use a Guess and Check table to solve this problem.

GC-69. Paul, Emilio, and Riki are three staff members at camp. Paul is three years older than Riki. Emilio is twice as old as Riki. The sum of Riki's age and Emilio's age is 81. How old is each person? Use a Guess and Check table to solve this problem. Remember to write your answer as a complete sentence.

GC-70.   Today the water level in the water tank is 9 feet high. **Three weeks ago** the water level was 15 feet.

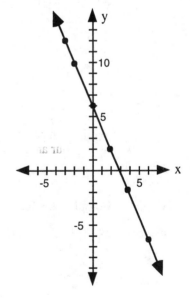

a)   What is the rate the water level drops each week? Assume the rate is constant.

b)   Copy the data table below and fill in the water levels for each week.

c)   Graph this situation.

Time (x) (in weeks)	-3	-2	-1	0	1	2	3	4	x
Water Level (y) (in feet)	15			9					y = -2x + 9

d)   Use the table or the graph to estimate during which week the water level will reach zero.

e)   Use your table and graph to estimate during which week the water level was approximately 20 feet. Why is the answer negative?

GC-71.   Use the graph shown below right to enter the ordered pairs in the table below.

x								x
y								

a)   Write the rule in words.

b)   Write the coordinates of the y-intercept. Remember that the y-intercept is where the line crosses the y-axis.

c)   Write the coordinates of the x-intercept. Remember that the x-intercept is where the line crosses the x-axis.

d)   Describe the direction of the line. What part of the equation tells you the direction of the line?

GC-72. Find the total area of the rectangle at right in as many different ways as you can. Explain your methods. Are there more than two ways to solve this problem?

GC-73. Merci has eight money envelopes, each labeled on the outside with the letter m. All the envelopes contain the same amount of money, but Merci does not know how much. She also has six more dollars in her purse.

a) Write an expression to represent how much money Merci has.

b) When Merci opens one of the envelopes, she finds $56 inside. How much money does Merci have altogether?

c) Write an equation to represent this situation.

GC-74. Use the order of operations and a table like the one at right to calculate the y-values. Follow the example as a model. Show all of your work.

x	y = 5 – 2x	y
-3	$y = 5 - 2(-3)$ $y = ⑤ - ②(-3)$ $y = ⑤ - (-6)$ $y = 11$	11
2		
-1		
0		

GC-75. Complete the following Diamond Problems.

Product

Sum

a)

b)

c)

d)

e)

GC-76. Which choice expresses 7% as a decimal?

(A) 0.07   (B) 0.7   (C) 7.0   (D) 700   (E) none of these

GC-77. Of the following numbers, which one best <u>approximates</u> 1084 −108.4?

(A) 10   (B) 100   (C) 1,000   (D) 10,000   (E) none of these

GC-78. Simplify each expression.

a) $(4x^2 + 2x + 6) + (x^2 + x + 10)$ b) $(3x + 4) + (x^2 + 6x + 2)$

c) $(6x^2 − 4x + 1) + (3x^2 + x − 7)$ d) $(2x^2 + 6) + (3x^2 − 6x)$

GC-79. Chad has six money envelopes with an x written on the outside of each one. He knows there is the same amount of money in each envelope, but he does not know how much. He also has five more dollars in his pocket.

a) Write an expression to represent how much money Chad has.

b) When Chad opens one of the envelopes, he finds $16 inside. Since each envelope contains the same amount of money, how much does he have altogether?

GC-80. The number of girls at camp was six more than twice the number of boys, and altogether there were 156 campers.

a) Use a Guess and Check table to find the number of boys and the number of girls at camp. Write your answer in a complete sentence.

b) Use your Guess and Check table and a variable to write an equation.

Going Camping: Algebraic Sentences

GC-81.   Johanna is planting tomatoes in the camp garden this year. At the nursery, tomato plants come in packs of six. She needs 80 plants in the garden and already has 26. How many packs of plants will she need?

a)   Use a Guess and Check table to solve this problem. Remember to write your answer as a complete sentence.

b)   Use your Guess and Check table to write an equation for the problem.

GC-82.   Guess Jeremiah's favorite number. He tells the campers, "If you multiply my number by 28 and then subtract 8, you end up with 160."

a)   Use a Guess and Check table to solve for his number. Be sure to write your answer as a sentence.

b)   Use your Guess and Check table to write an equation that represents this situation.

GC-83.

WRITING EQUATIONS FROM A GUESS AND CHECK TABLE

- Make a Guess and Check table and solve the problem. Use at least four guesses, show all of your work, and write your answer in a complete sentence.

- Put an x in your Guess column and use x to write expressions in each of the other columns.

- Write your equation outside the Guess and Check table. You may need to use the Distributive Property and/or combine like terms.

Example: Noel and his sister, Brigitte, are both at camp. Noel is 3 years older than Brigitte, and the sum of their ages is 21. How old is Noel and how old is Brigitte? Use a Guess and Check table to solve for their ages. Write an equation.

Guess Brigitte's Age	Noel's Age	Sum of Noel and Brigitte's Ages	Check 21
10	$(10) + 3 = 13$	$(10) + (13) = 23$	too high
5	$(5) + 3 = 8$	$(5) + (8) = 13$	too low
8	$(8) + 3 = 11$	$(8) + (11) = 19$	too low
9	$(9) + 3 = 12$	$(9) + (12) = 21$	correct
x	$x + 3$	$(x) + (x + 3) = 21$	

$$(x) + (x + 3) = 2x + 3 = 21$$

Noel is 12 years old and Brigitte is nine years old.

Make these notes in your Tool Kit to the right of the double-lined box.

List three important things for you to remember when writing equations.

GC-84. Compute.

a) -8 + 2

b) 7 – 11

c) -5 + (-8)

d) -3 – 9

e) 6 – (-5)

f) (6) · (-2)

g) -7 – 4

h) -8 + 8

i) -24 ÷ -8

j) -16 ÷ 4

GC-85. Draw a spinner that would show the results of tossing one die (singular for "dice").

a) How many sections should you have on the spinner?

b) What is the probability of landing on any one of the sections?

c) Write an equation to show that the sum of all the probabilities is equal to 1.

d) What is the probability of spinning a 4? Write your answer as a fraction and a percent.

e) What is the probability of spinning either a 2 or a 3? Write your answer as a fraction and a percent.

f) If you spin the spinner and roll a real die, what is the probability of getting a 5 and a 4? Write your answer as a fraction and a percent

GC-86. Use the order of operations and a table like the one at right to calculate the y-values. Use the example given as a model. Show all of your work.

x	$y = x^2 + 1$	y
-3		
-2	$y = (-2)^2 + 1$	
	$y = \boxed{(-2)^2} + \boxed{1}$	
	$y = \boxed{4} + \boxed{1}$	
	$y = 5$	5
-1		
0		
1		

GC-87.   Use a resource page or copy and complete the table using the Distributive Property. Use algebra tiles if you need them.

Factored Form	Distributed	Simplified
6(4 + x)	6(4) + 6(x)	24 + 6x
3x(x + 3)	3x(x) + 3x(3)	
6(2x + 3)		
5(2x + 4)		
	4(x) + 4(2)	
x(x + 8)		
3(2x + 2)		

GC-88.   Examine the rectangle shown at right.

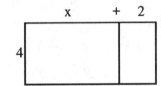

a)   Express the total area of the rectangle in two different ways. Explain your methods.

b)   Assume the area is 28 square units and write an equation.

c)   What is the value of x?

GC-89.   Margaurite wants to convince her parents to raise her monthly allowance. She decided to take a quick poll of her five best friends to see what they thought. Here are the results:

Friend	Suggested Allowance
Kari	no allowance
Wanda	$25.00
Gary	$100.00
Donna	$20.00
Jorge	$20.00

a)   Calculate the mean, median, and mode for her friends' suggested allowances.

b)   Calculate the range of her friends' suggested allowances.

c)   Her current allowance is $30.00. Which measure of central tendency supports her argument? Why?

GC-90.   Find areas A and B in the figure at right when the rectangle is cut by the lines shown. (All dimensions are in centimeters.)

GC-91. These problems were done in class as a mental math exercise. If you were not in class, copy each problem. Close your book, and then solve.

a) $6 \cdot 55$

b) $7 \cdot 51$

c) $3 \cdot 58$

d) $31 \cdot 8$

e) $7 \cdot 39$

f) $4 \cdot 26$

GC-92.

Mr. Martin, the head groundskeeper at camp, mows the camp lawn. The lawn is rectangular, and the length is 5 feet more than twice the width. The perimeter of the lawn is 250 feet. What are the dimensions of the lawn?

a) Draw and label a diagram of the lawn.

b) Use a Guess and Check table to help you find the dimensions of the lawn.

c) Next, replace your guesses with x and write an equation to represent the problem. Show all steps as you combine like terms to simplify the equation.

d) What are the dimensions of the lawn? Write your answer in a complete sentence.

e) Use the dimensions from part (d) to find the area of the lawn. Write your answer in a complete sentence.

GC-93. Tito and Rudy were playing the "guess my number" game. Tito says, "I'm thinking of a number. If you add my number to 11 and then multiply the sum by 2, you get 47." He added, "My number is not a whole number. What is my number?"

a) Use a Guess and Check table to help Rudy find Tito's number.

b) Write an equation to represent the problem.

c) What is Tito's number? Write your answer in a complete sentence.

GC-94.   Notice that we can find the perimeter of the figure below by counting the number of lengths between the dots around the outside and that we can find the area by counting all the squares inside.

The perimeter is 14 units.
The area is eight square units.

A local rancher supplies some of the food for the camp. Below are models of his land and the crops he grows. Find the perimeter and area for each of the figures below. Include "units" for perimeter and "square units" for area.

a)   Corn Field

b)   Tomato Field

GC-95.   There are two or more ways to find the areas of the figures below. Find the area of each figure using at least two models. Show all subproblems.

a)   2 + 6

4
+
1

b)   3 + 3 + 3

6
+
3

GC-96.   Use the resource page or copy and complete the table below. Use the Distributive Property to complete the blank spaces. The first problem is done for you.

Factored Form	Distributed	Simplified
7(n + 3)	7(n) + 7(3)	7n + 21
2(2p + 3)	2(2p) + 2(3)	
4(g − 5)		4g − 20
-2(x + 4)		-2x − 8
x(4 + 5)		9x
5x(x + 2)		$5x^2 + 10x$

CHAPTER 4

GC-97. Copy this table and use the order of operations to complete it. Use the example given as a model. Show all of your work for each y-value.

x	$y = x^2 + 2x$	y
-4		8
-3		
-2	$y = (-2)^2 + 2(-2)$ $y = \boxed{(-2)^2} + \boxed{2(-2)}$ $y = \boxed{4} + \boxed{-4}$ $y = 0$	0
-1		-1
0		0
1		
2		8
3		

GC-98. Use your ordered pairs from the table in the previous problem to graph the equation $y = x^2 + 2x$.

a) What are the x-intercepts?   b) What is the y-intercept?

GC-99. Matt had nine money envelopes with the letter q written on the outside of each one. Each envelope contained the same amount of money. In addition to the money in the envelopes, he had 17 dollars.

a) Write a variable expression to represent the amount of money Matt had.

b) One of Matt's friends told him he knew Matt had a total of $179. Write an equation to represent the total amount of money Matt had.

c) How much money was in each of the envelopes? Write your answer in a complete sentence.

GC-100. The area of a square is 81 square inches. What is its perimeter?

(A) 36 inches   (B) 9 inches   (C) 20.5 inches   (D) 18 inches   (E) none of these

GC-101. On Monday, Jake read x pages of his book. On Tuesday, he read y pages of the book. On Wednesday, he read z pages of the book. How many pages did Jake read altogether?

(A) xyz   (B) x + y + z   (C) 3xyz   (D) 3x + y + z   (E) none of these

GC-102. Tyler was using number tiles to help him find the solution to a **Target Game**. The number tiles he was using were 2, 6, and 8. His target number was 7. He was so excited when he found the solution that he knocked his desk over and spilled the tiles everywhere. "I know I had the solution and I remember what it looked like, but I don't remember where each number went. I'll draw the shape of my expression to help me remember." Where had Tyler put the numbers to hit his target number of 7?

$$\frac{\square + \square}{\square} = 7$$

GC-103. The **factors** of 12 are 1, 2, 3, 4, 6, and 12. The factors of 20 are 1, 2, 4, 5, 10, and 20.

a) Write down what you think a factor is.

b) List the factors of the number 30.

GC-104. List the factors of:

a) 24 b) 15 c) 36 d) 13

GC-105. Teresa has 36 square tiles on her desk that she is arranging into rectangles. She must use all 36 tiles for each rectangle she makes.

a) Draw all the possible rectangles that Teresa could make.

b) List the dimensions (factor pairs) of each rectangle you found.

GC-106.

DISTRIBUTIVE PROPERTY

The **DISTRIBUTIVE PROPERTY** shows how to express sums and products in two ways: $a(b + c) = ab + ac$. This can also be written $(b + c) a = ab + ac$.

Factored form	Distributed form	Simplified form
a(b + c)	**a(b) + a(c)**	**ab + ac**

To simplify: Multiply each term on the inside of the parentheses by the term on the outside. Combine terms if possible.

To factor: Find a common factor that divides each term evenly. Then write this factor outside the parentheses and leave the remaining factors of each term written as a sum.

Note: An **integer factor** is an integer that divides another integer evenly.

Examples: Simplify: $5(x + 12)$ Factor: $4x + 6$ Factor: $6x + 3$

$$5(x + 12)$$
$$⑤(x) + ⑤(12)$$
$$5x + 60$$

$$4x + 6$$
$$2(2x) + 2(3)$$
$$②(2x) + ②(3)$$
$$2(2x + 3)$$

$$6x + 3$$
$$3(2x) + 3(1)$$
$$③(2x) + ③(1)$$
$$3(2x + 1)$$

Make these notes in your Tool Kit to the right of the double-lined box.

a) List two examples of pairs of numbers that share a common factor.

b) List a variable pair with a common factor. Check your examples with your partner or a teammate to verify that they are correct.

c) Why do you think $ab + ac$ is called the "simplified form"?

GC-107. Simplify the following problems.

a) $(2x + 4)6$

b) $7(x - 3)$

c) $-8(9x - 7)$

d) $-4(13 - x)$

GC-108. Factor the following expressions.

a) $2x + 20$

b) $5x + 35$

c) $3x - 15$

d) $5x - 60$

GC-109. You have been using the Distributive Property to simplify expressions throughout this chapter. Now you will reverse the order to put the expressions into **factored form**. The factors show what is being multiplied before distribution takes place. Use the Distributive Property to complete the table below. Use the resource page or your paper.

Factored Form	Distributed	Simplified
3(x + 1)	3(x) + 3(1)	3x + 3
	2(x) + 2(3)	2x + 6
		5x + 15
		6x + 12
		9c + 27
		8b + 16
		2x – 6
		-3x + 9

GC-110. Melvin had 22 money envelopes with the letter x written on the outside of each one. Each contained the same amount of money. He also had an extra $8.00 hidden in the fold of his wallet.

a) Write an expression to represent the amount of money Melvin had.

b) When Melvin opened one of the envelopes, there was a bill for $12. Write a number that expresses the amount he owed.

c) Substitute the value into the expression you wrote in part (a) to determine how much money he had.

GC-111. Katrina was using some algebra tiles. She had three large squares, five rectangles, and eight small squares on her desk. Xyrus stopped by and dropped a small bag of tiles on her desk that contained six large squares, three rectangles, and seven small squares. Write an algebraic equation to show the tiles with which Katrina started, the tiles that Xyrus gave her, and the total number of tiles she now has on her desk. To see what to write, refer to problem GC-44.

GC-112. Copy this table and use the order of operations to complete it. Using the example given as a model, show all of your work for each y-value.

x	$y = x^2 + 2x + 1$	y
-2	$y = (-2)^2 + 2(-2) + 1$	
	$y = (-2)^2 + (2(-2)) + (1)$	
	$y = (4) + (-4) + (1)$	
	$y = 1$	1
-1		
0		
1		

GC-113. Use the ordered pairs from your table in the previous problem and at least four additional pairs.

a) Graph the rule $y = x^2 + 2x + 1$.   b) Describe the shape of the graph.

GC-114. The camp council is designing a patio floor for an outdoor cafeteria. They have chosen the pattern shown at right.

a) What is the area of the section with the pattern?

b) What are the factors (dimensions) of the section?

c) What is the area of the section with the ▓ pattern?

d) What are the factors (dimensions) of the ▓ section?

e) Notice that there are two sections of the patio in the ▧ pattern. What is the combined area of those sections?

GC-115. Write this expression as simply as you can: $\dfrac{3! + 4!}{6!}$

(5! means $1 \cdot 2 \cdot 3 \cdot 4 \cdot 5$.)

GC-116. Compute.

a) $(-1) \cdot 3$ b) $(-1) \cdot (-4)$

c) $(-1) \cdot 23$ d) $(-1) \cdot x$

e) $-1(5x + 3)$ f) $-1(x + 6)$

GC-117. Describe the effect on an integer or variable when it is multiplied by a negative one.

GC-118. Compute the product in column A and compare it with the result in column B. Follow the examples in parts (a) and (b) as you complete parts (c) through (f).

Column A (Distribute and multiply by -1.)	Column B (Take the opposite of each term inside the parentheses.)
a) $-1(x + 8) = (-1)x + (-1)(8)$ $= -x + (-8)$ $= -x - 8$	$-(x + 8) = -x + (-8) = -x - 8$
b) $-1(x - 7) = (-1)(x) - (-1)(7)$ $= -x - (-7)$ $= -x + 7$	$-(x - 7) = -x - (-7) = -x + 7$
c) $(-1)(2x - 11)$	$-(2x - 11) = \underline{\hspace{1.5cm}} = \underline{\hspace{1cm}}$
d) $(-1)(-3x + 10)$	$-(-3x + 10) = \underline{\hspace{1.5cm}} = \underline{\hspace{1cm}}$
e) $(-1)(2x^2 - 24x + 4)$	$-(2x^2 - 24x + 4) = \underline{\hspace{1.5cm}} = \underline{\hspace{1cm}}$
f) $(-1)(6 - 5x)$	$-(6 - 5x) = \underline{\hspace{1.5cm}} = \underline{\hspace{1cm}}$

g) Write an equation to show the relationship between $-(a + b)$ and $-a - b$.

h) Write an equation to show the relationship between $(-1)(a - b)$ and $-a + b$.

GC-119.

Chapter Summary When you finish a chapter in a math course, you need to reflect on how well you have learned the material. It is time to think about all that you have studied and learned in this chapter.

With your partner or team, find the problem assigned by your teacher. After you have verified that you have a correct solution from your (or a teammate's) work, use the model below to create a summary poster of the mathematical idea you were assigned.

Write out the mathematical idea for your problem number and record the problem number.

Show all of the mathematical work and diagrams you used to solve the problem.

Topic: Problem #	
Solution	Explanation

Describe each step of your solution in words.

GC-120. Joann, the camp supply manager, is ordering replacement backpacks. Based on her inventory, Joann will order twelve more green packs than blue packs, four times as many black packs as blue packs, and two times as many orange packs as black packs and blue packs together. She will order a total of 204 backpacks.

a) Use a Guess and Check table to help you find the number of each color backpack Joann needs to order.

b) Use your Guess and Check table to help write a variable expression to represent the number of backpacks of each color.

c) Write an equation to represent this problem. Show all steps as you combine like terms to simplify the equation.

d) How many backpacks of each color should Joann order? Write your answer in a complete sentence.

e) Joann can buy the backpacks for $6.50 through a wholesale catalog company. She has a budget of $1,425. Will she be able to buy the backpacks needed? Write your answer in a complete sentence.

f) If the backpacks are mixed together in one crate, what is the probability that Joann would unpack a black one first?

GC-121.

DISTRIBUTING A NEGATIVE ONE

When a negative one (-1) is distributed to the terms inside a pair of parentheses, the sign of <u>each</u> term is changed. For example,

$-(3x^2 + 2x - 5) \Rightarrow (-1)(3x^2 + 2x - 5) \Rightarrow (-1)(3x^2) + (-1)(2x) - (-1)(5) \Rightarrow -3x^2 - 2x + 5$

Answer these questions in your Tool Kit to the right of the double-lined box.

a) How does distributing a negative one relate to subtraction?

b) What happens to a term or number when it is multiplied by negative one?

GC-122. Compute.

a) -(34)

b) -(5x - 12)

c) $-(2x^2 - 5x + 1)$

GC-123.   Solve the following exercises for x:

a) $|-15| = x$ b) $|x| = 15$

c) $|x| = -4$ d) $|x| = x$

e)   Use a number line to show the solutions to $|x| = 7$.

GC-124.   Stefano and Leo want to use different shades of blue tiles to build a rectangular mosaic with an area of 375 square feet. Stefano suggested that the length of one side should be 10 feet longer than the length of the other side. Find the dimensions (length and width) of their mosaic.

a)   Draw and label a diagram.

b)   Make a Guess and Check table to solve the problem.

c)   Use your Guess and Check table to write an equation.

GC-125.   Use the Distributive Property to simplify the following problems. Combine like terms where possible.

a) $(3x + 7 + 9)2$ b) $7.5(3) + 7.5(6)$

c) $6(x) + 6(20)$ d) $2(6) + 2(-4)$

e) $4(3x - 11 + 9)$ f) $1.5(3) + 1.5(6)$

GC-126.   Hannah, the camp cook, uses a standard recipe for trail mix that uses raisins, chocolate pieces, and peanuts. The quantity of chocolate pieces is 4 ounces more than 3 times the number of ounces of raisins. The quantity of peanuts is 5 ounces less than twice the number of ounces of raisins. Use a Guess and Check table to find the quantity of each ingredient Hannah uses in her standard recipe.

a)   What variable would you use to represent the quantity of raisins?

b)   Use that variable to write an algebraic expression that represents the quantity of chocolate pieces.

c)   Use that same variable to write an algebraic expression that represents the quantity of peanuts.

d)   Use the algebraic expressions you wrote in parts (a), (b), and (c) above to write a single expression for all the ingredients.

>>**Problem continues on the next page.**>>

e)   Simplify your expression.

f)   Hannah's standard recipe makes 95 ounces of trail mix. Use your simplified expression in part (e) to write an equation that represents her recipe.

g)   Use your equation in part (f) to find the quantity (in ounces) of raisins in Hannah's recipe. Any strategy is acceptable. Show your work. h)   Now find the quantity (in ounces) of chocolate pieces and peanuts.

GC-127.   The camp director asked Hannah to put more peanuts into her trail mix.

a)   Use your variable for raisins to write a new expression for peanuts if the number of ounces of peanuts is now going to be 7 ounces more than twice the number of ounces of raisins.

b)   Find the total amount of each ingredient needed now.

GC-128.   This year 78 of the campers have decided to construct a new border around the swimming pool. Each camper will construct one block of tile pieces like the pattern shown at right. How many total tiles are needed?

This is how Chad set up the problem:

78 campers(4 waffle tiles) + 78(3 dotted tiles) + 78(2 wavy tiles) = 78(4) + 78(3) + 78(2)

This is how Scooter set up the problem:

78 campers(4 waffle tiles + 3 dotted tiles + 2 wavy tiles) = 78(4 + 3 + 2)

a)   What will Chad's answer be?

b)   What will Scooter's answer be?

c)   Who had the correct set-up? How do you know?

d)   If each tile costs $2, compute the total cost of purchasing tiles to complete the project.

GC-129.   Lauren had 12 money envelopes with the letter b written on the outside of each. Each envelope contained the same amount. She also had three dollars more in her purse. Lauren had a total of $21.

a)   Make a Guess and Check table to help you find the amount of money in each envelope.

b)   Write your answer in a complete sentence.

c)   Write an equation to represent this problem.

GC-130. Show two methods for finding the area of the rectangles below. Be sure to write and label your subproblems.

a)

```
      5  +   7
  ┌────────┬────────┐
2 │        │        │
  └────────┴────────┘
```

b)

```
      10 +   15
  ┌────────┬────────┐
6 │        │        │
  └────────┴────────┘
```

GC-131. Belinda has four money envelopes with the letter m written on the outside of each one. Each envelope contains the same amount of money. She also has $30 in her pocket.

a) Write an expression to represent how much money Belinda has.

b) After Belinda opens all the envelopes, she finds she has only $10 left. Assuming there was the same amount in each envelope, what amount was in each envelope?

GC-132. Allesandro and Irene were given the task of designing one of the small rectangular mosaics for the outside wall of the camp post office. They are told that the area of the planned mosaic will be 480 square inches. The short side is four inches shorter than the long side. Help Allesandro and Irene figure out the dimensions of the mosaic they will build.

a) List the pairs of integer factors of 480.

b) Use your results from part (a) and a Guess and Check table (if needed) to find the dimensions of the mosaic.

c) Use x to write an equation for this problem.

GC-133. Use the Distributive Property to simplify or factor.

a) $43(3 + 2x)$ b) $8(15 - 6x)$

c) $5x + 25$ d) $(7x - 5)4$

e) $11(9 + 8x)$ f) $4x - 28$

GC-134. Harry wants to lead a group around the lake. He is not sure if it will be a day hike or an overnight trip. Fred tells him that if you take the distance around the lake, add 2, and multiply the answer by 15, the total number of miles will be equal to the number of campers in this session. Harry knows that there are 480 campers, so now he can figure out the distance around the lake.

a) Use a Guess and Check table to figure out the distance around the lake. Do not forget to write your answer in a sentence.

b) Use your Guess and Check table to write an equation.

c) Should the hike be a day hike or an overnight hike? Write your answer in a complete sentence.

GC-135. **What We Have Done in This Chapter**

Below is a list of the Tool Kit entries from this chapter.

- GC-6   Order of Operations
- GC-18   Distributive Property with Integers
- GC-43   How to Combine Like Terms
- GC-57   Distributive Property with Algebra Tiles
- GC-83   Writing Equations from a Guess and Check Table
- GC-106   Distributive Property
- GC-121   Distributing a Negative One

Review all the entries and read the notes you made in your Tool Kit. Make a list of any questions, terms, or notes you do not understand. Ask your partner or study team members for help. If anything is still unclear, ask your teacher.

Chapter 5

Chapter 5
The Math Club: SOLVING EQUATIONS

In this chapter you will learn how to solve equations. You will have the opportunity to see the connection between algebraic and graphic solutions. You will finish the first half of the course by reviewing the five chapters you have studied thus far.

In this chapter you will have the opportunity to:

- write and solve multiple types of equations.
- simplify expressions using the Distributive Property.
- investigate inverse operations.
- review the topics studied in the first half of the course.

Read the problem below, but **do not try to solve it now**. What you learn over the next few days will enable you to solve it.

MC-0.   The Mental Math Club is a very active club! Every year the members design a new t-shirt to wear on field trips and at math competitions. There are three companies in town that make t-shirts: *Tanks A Lot*, *Screeners*, and *Teesers*. What criteria can Diedre, the club president, use to decide from which company to order the shirts?

Number Sense		
Algebra and Functions		
Mathematical Reasoning		
Measurement and Geometry		
Statistics, Data Analysis, & Probability		

MC-1.   **Mental Math** What value of the variable makes each equation true? Solve each equation in your head.

a) $4x = 12$

b) $x + 13 = 20$

c) $5x = 35$

d) $2x = -17$

e) $3x + 7 = 15$

f) $2x + 3 = x - 8$

g)   Which equations were most difficult to solve mentally? Explain.

MC-2.   The members of the Mental Math Club want to raise money so they can take a trip. They decide to sell t-shirts with a logo. Diedre, the president of the club, calls two t-shirt vendors to find out how much it will cost to make the shirts. *Screeners* charges a setup fee of $50 to prepare the silk-screen for the logo. In addition, *Screeners* charges $7 for each shirt imprinted with the logo. The second vendor Diedre called, *Teesers*, charges $78 for the setup fee and $5 for each t-shirt.

a)   If Diedre wants to order 10 shirts to sell at school, should she buy the shirts from *Screeners* or *Teesers*? Give reasons for your answer.

b)   If Diedre wants to order 20 shirts to sell at school, should she buy the shirts from *Screeners* or *Teesers*? Give reasons for your answer.

c)   Determine the number of t-shirts that make the total cost from each vendor equal. You can use a Guess and Check table like the one below.

Number of T-Shirts	Cost at Screeners	Cost at Teesers	Same?

d)   Tell Diedre which company she should choose. Explain your reasoning so she can make the best choice.

MC-3.   Sometimes you can make a math problem easier by replacing part of it with an **equivalent** quantity. For example, you could describe the distance from San Francisco to Los Angeles as 379 miles or as 2,001,120 feet. Two expressions are equivalent if they represent the same number. Twelve inches is equivalent to 1 foot, 4 quarts is equivalent to 1 gallon, and 379 miles is equivalent to 2,001,120 feet.

a)   Thirty-two ounces is equivalent to how many pounds?

b)   One century is equivalent to how many years?

c)   Ten weeks is equivalent to how many days?

d)   Marty says her baby weighs 8 pounds. The scale shows 128 ounces. Is 8 pounds equivalent to 128 ounces? Show your work.

MC-4.   For parts (a) and (b) below write an equation that shows
         the indicated equivalencies.

   a)   How many minutes is two hours?

   b)   How many seconds is two hours?

   c)   Explain why 120 minutes = 7200 seconds.

MC-5.   Bradley and Mindy are siblings who enjoy
         doing many things together. Write a
         numerical equation that describes each of the
         following situations.

   a)   Bradley challenged Mindy to a basketball
         game. Mindy made four three-point
         shots. Bradley made five two-point shots
         and two free throws (1 point each). At
         that point, the score was tied. Write an
         equation showing that the two scores are
         equivalent.

   b)   They continued playing for ten minutes
         and both scored four more two-point
         shots. Write an equation that shows the two new scores are equivalent. Who won?

   c)   Bradley and Mindy went to the arcade. Mindy won twelve tickets on one game and
         eight on another. Bradley won five tickets on one game, five tickets on another
         game, and ten tickets on a third game. Are their totals equivalent? Write an equation
         to justify your answer.

   d)   In the next ten minutes Bradley and Mindy each double their total tickets. Do they
         then have an equivalent number of tickets? Explain your answer.

   e)   Bradley brought a twenty-dollar bill. Bradley spent one-fourth of his money.
         Mindy brought seventeen dollars but lost two dollars. Do they have equivalent
         amounts of money? Explain your answer.

MC-6. Sam plays golf at least five times a week. He records his score for each round of golf. Here are the scores for his last ten rounds:

Round	1	2	3	4	5	6	7	8	9	10
Score	73	74	67	67	74	74	72	75	66	68

a) Determine the mean, median, and mode for Sam's scores.

b) Determine the range of Sam's scores.

c) Par for the course is 72. How far from par are the mean, median, and mode?

d) Does Sam usually score above or below par? Explain.

MC-7. Bill is expecting 60 people for a barbecue. He purchased 60 burgers and 60 buns. The number of burgers is equivalent to the number of buns. Two days before the event Bill learns that 45% more people are expected to come. How many more buns and burgers does Bill need to buy?

MC-8.

EQUATIONS

A mathematical sentence with an equal sign is called an **EQUATION**. It is a relationship showing that two expressions have the same value.

Statements like 16 ounces = 1 pound, $n = 4$, $3(x - 5) = 16$, and $3(2) + 7 = 16 - 3$ are examples of equations.

Make these notes in your Tool Kit to the right of the double-lined box.

Write four equations that illustrate the equivalence of two quantities.

MC-9.   Complete the tables below and graph each of the equations. Review your Tool Kit to be
         sure you make a complete graph.

    a)   y = 2x + 5

x	0	1	2	3	-1	-2	-3
y	5	7					

    b)   y = x - 2

x	0		4	-1		2	-3	
y		-1.5		-4				-2.5

MC-10.   Solve each equation for x. Show or explain your thinking. The ability to explain your
         methods will help you as you develop new methods for solving equations.

    a)   x + 23 = 50   b)   2x = 92

    c)   3x + 25 = 100   d)   72 = 6x

MC-11.   Now that we have started a new chapter, it is time for you to
         organize your binder.

    a)   Put the work from the last chapter in order and keep it in a
          separate folder.

    b)   When this is completed, write, "I have organized my binder."

MC-12.   Follow your teacher's directions for practicing mental math. Explain which multiplication
         strategy you like best and why you like the strategy.

MC-13.   Work backward to find the missing number.

    a)   Alcania is thinking of a number. If you double it and take away four, the result
          is 28. What is Alcania's number?

    b)   Omar is thinking of a number. Take half of the number, then add 12. The result is
          37. Find Omar's number.

MC-14. **Cover-Up Method** The Mental Math Club was planning a carnival to raise money. Jacob decided to run the Guess My Number booth. His good friend Carlin wanted to check out the booth before the carnival opened for business. "Try out a problem on me," said Carlin.

Jacob gave Carlin this problem: "17 more than a number is 52. Guess the number and win a prize." Carlin pictured it like this: $x + 17 = 52$

Carlin covered up the x and asked himself, "What number plus 17 equals 52? Aha," he said, "x equals 35."

$$(?) + 17 = 52$$
$$x = 35$$

He put 35 back into the equation and discovered he was right, because $35 + 17 = 52$.

$$(35) + 17 = 52$$

"That was too easy!" exclaimed Carlin. "We won't make any money if the problems are this easy. You need to make them harder. Show me the other problems you had in mind."

Help Carlin check to see if these problems are also too easy. Use Carlin's cover-up method to solve each problem. Be sure to put your answers back into the original equations to check your work.

a) $x + 7 = 13$

b) $x - 6 = 18$

c) $y + 22 = 39$

d) $s + 25 = 155$

e) $r - 12 = 38$

f) $m - 15 = -60$

g) $x - 36 = -30$

h) $x + 40 = -10$

i) $z + \frac{5}{7} = 3$

MC-15. Jacob pulled out his second set of problems. "These are harder. Try this one."

"Four more than three times the number is 40."

Carlin pictured the problem like this: $\qquad\qquad\qquad$ $3x + 4 = 40$

He had to break this problem down into more than one step.

First he covered up the term with the unknown. He asked $\qquad$ $(?) + 4 = 40$
himself what number plus 4 equals 40. "Oh," he said, "That's $\qquad$ $(36) + 4 = 40$
easy. Thirty-six plus four equals 40, so $3x$ must equal 36." $\qquad\quad$ $3x = 36$

However, Carlin was not finished. He still had to find out what
number the unknown x represented. So he covered up the x in $\qquad$ $3 \cdot (?) = 36$
$3x$, asking himself, "Three multiplied by what number equals $\qquad$ $3 \cdot (12) = 36$
36?" This was not difficult. He knew that 3 times 12 is 36, so x $\qquad\quad$ $x = 12$
must equal 12.

He checked his answer by substituting 12 for x. Since this was $\qquad$ $3(12) + 4 = 40$
correct, he knew he had found the correct value for x. $\qquad\qquad$ $36 + 4 = 40$

"These are better," claimed Carlin. "Let me see the rest of them." Use Carlin's cover-up method to check the rest of Jacob's problems. Write each step.

a) $\quad 6x - 7 = 35$ $\qquad$ b) $\quad 3x + 8 = 23$ $\qquad$ c) $\quad \frac{c}{2} + 20 = 38$

d) $\quad 8x + 14 = -10$ $\qquad$ e) $\quad 102m + 102 = 306$ $\qquad$ f) $\quad \frac{x}{20} + 17 = 257$

g) $\quad 3x - 2 = 13$ $\qquad$ h) $\quad 5x + 4 = -26$ $\qquad$ i) $\quad 2x + \frac{1}{5} = 1$

MC-16. Ingrid bought three dozen donuts for the Mental
Math Club meeting. Twenty-four people showed up
for the meeting. How many donuts did each person
get? Assume each person gets the same amount.

a) Which equation best represents this problem?

(1) $x = 36 + 24$ $\quad$ (2) $36x = 24$ $\quad$ (3) $24x = 36$

b) Solve the equation you chose in part (a) to find
the answer.

c) Is your answer for part (b) reasonable?
Explain.

MC-17. Compute.

    a)   -24 ÷ 6   b)   3 + (-5)   c)   -4 – (-6)   d)   13 – 6

    e)   -14 ÷ (-7)   f)   7 – (-8)   g)   5 + (-2)   h)   -8 – (-4)

    i)   (-9)(-2)   j)   (-6)(6)

MC-18. The number $1\frac{2}{3}$ is a mixed number that means "one whole and two-thirds of another whole." We can draw a picture to illustrate $1\frac{2}{3}$, as shown at right.

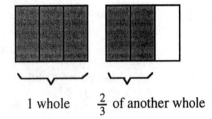

1 whole $\frac{2}{3}$ of another whole

    a)   How many one-thirds are in $1\frac{2}{3}$?

    b)   Sketch a picture to represent $1\frac{3}{4}$.   c)   How many one-fourths are in $1\frac{3}{4}$?

    d)   Sketch a picture to illustrate $3\frac{4}{5}$.   e)   How many one-fifths are in $3\frac{4}{5}$?

MC-19. Manuela is helping to prepare for the "Come as your favorite mathematician" party by filling piñatas with candy. In each piñata she includes 50 hard candies, 20 suckers, 35 jawbreakers, 60 mini candy bars, 25 sour balls, and 75 pieces of bubble gum. If Manuela is going to fill four piñatas, how many pieces of candy does she need? Write the number of candies she needs in two different ways using the Distributive Property.

MC-20. Antonio and Anna are working on a problem when they decide that they need to combine their algebra tiles in order to work it out. Antonio puts four rectangles and nine small squares on the desk. Anna puts two rectangles and three small squares on the desk. Draw a diagram and write an algebraic equation that represents what each team member put on the desk as well as the combined total.

MC-21. What is the product of $\frac{6}{7} \cdot 42$?

    (A) 36   (B) 49   (C) 252   (D) 294   (E) none of these

MC-22. Which of the following integers is closest to $\frac{31}{7}$?

    (A) 3   (B) 4   (C) 5   (D) 6

MC-23. These questions relate to dividing by 4. Some of them may not be possible. If they are not, explain why not in a sentence or two.

a) Find all digits that make the number 42,3__1 divisible by 4.

b) Find all digits that make the number 43,__00 divisible by 4.

c) Suppose you know that the number N is divisible by 4. (That is, there is some integer M such that $4 \cdot M = N$.) Is the number $N + 400$ also divisible by 4? Explain your answer using complete sentences.

d) Suppose you know that the number N is **not** divisible by 4. Can the number $N + 400$ be divisible by 4? Explain your answer using complete sentences.

MC-24. Follow your teacher's directions for practicing mental math. Describe the strategy you used to your partner or study team member.

MC-25. Hakim has two identical boxes of stuffed toys to use as prizes at the carnival. He has already given away 22 prizes from one box. Hakim now has 128 prizes left. How many prizes were in each box before the carnival opened? Write an equation like Carlin's from yesterday and solve it using the cover-up method.

MC-26. Carlin felt that there needed to be some problems that were even more difficult for the people who had already won at the Guess My Number booth. He wrote down the following number sentence: $3x - 15 = 30$.

He needed to change the symbols into a word clue for the booth. Carlin's translation is: "If you triple my number and subtract 15, you end up with 30. What is my number?" Change the rest of Carlin's number sentences into clues for the booth.

a) $8x + 32 = 104$ b) $\frac{x}{12} + 18 = 30$ c) $\frac{(x + 4)}{6} = 4$

d) $\frac{(x + 2)}{6} + 6 = 12$ e) $-9x - 10 = -82$

MC-27.   Take Carlin's equations from the previous problem and use the cover-up method to find
          the missing numbers. Be sure to put the numbers back into the original equations to
          check that they are correct.

MC-28.   Admission into the carnival is $5 for adults and $2 for
          children. The carnival offers a special family pack
          which admits 2 adults and 3 children for one price of
          $14.

          a)   If you are in a group of 12 adults and 15
                children, should you buy the family pack,
                individual tickets, or combinations of them?

          b)   What should you purchase if you are in a group
                with 5 adults and 30 children?

MC-29.   Six members of a Sumo wrestling team weighed themselves and discovered that the
          sum of their combined weights totaled 30 pounds less than one ton (2000 pounds).
          Boyd weighed 20 pounds more than twice Trede's weight. Kerber weighed 40
          pounds less than Adam. Smith and Craig each weighed five pounds more than
          Kerber. Adam weighed 35 pounds less than twice Trede. Trede is the smallest of the
          six guys. Use a Guess and Check table to find out how much each player weighs.

MC-30.   Janae invited five friends to her house so all six of
          them could make bead necklaces. She bought a bag
          containing 750 beads and she wants to distribute the
          beads evenly. How many beads does each person
          get? Write an equation, then solve it.

MC-31.   Solve each equation for x. Check your solution.

          a) $2x + 8 = 16$ b) $2 = 3x - 13$

          c) $22 = 4x + 2$ d) $3x - 5 = 16$

          e) $-19 = 21 + 10x$ f) $\dfrac{x - 5}{6} = 3$

MC-32. Miranda and Tasha were responsible for ordering last year's Math Club t-shirts. They knew they had ordered 15 more red shirts than white shirts and twice as many blue shirts as white shirts for the 63 members. Unfortunately, the shirts arrived late and it was summer vacation. All of the shirts ended up in one big box because Miranda and Tasha were not around to sort them.

a) How many of each type of shirt did they order? (Use a Guess and Check table if necessary).

b) What percentage of the total order was red shirts?

c) If Miranda reaches into the box, what is the probability of pulling out a blue shirt?

d) If Tasha reaches into the box, what is the probability of pulling out a color other than white?

MC-33. Find the missing fraction, decimal, or percent for the following problems.

a)
30%

b)
0.625

c)
$\frac{2}{8}$

MC-34. Add or subtract as indicated.

a) $5\frac{3}{4} + 2\frac{3}{4}$

b) $9 - 6\frac{1}{4}$

c) $4\frac{7}{8} + 5\frac{5}{24}$

d) $15\frac{1}{3} - 12\frac{3}{4}$

MC-35. Simplify each of the following expressions.

a) $(4x^2 + 2x + 1) + (x - 8)$

b) $(3x^2 - 2x + 7) - (2x^2 + 3x + 1)$

MC-36. Use the cover-up method to solve the equations below.

a) $2x + 5 = 25$

b) $14 = 5x - 31$

c) $4x + 22 = 6$

MC-37. Complete these equations.

a) $1\frac{1}{2}$ ft. = ___ inches   b) $3\frac{3}{4}$ days = ___ hours   c) 60 hours = ___ days

MC-38. You are going to practice a system for solving equations that will be modeled by your teacher.

a) On the balance scale below, the circles represent cups with an unknown number of positive or negative tiles inside. The cups all have the same number of tiles in them. How many cups can we remove from both sides and still maintain balance? Use the resource page to complete the problem.

b) The balance scale now looks like this:

What can we remove from (or add to) both sides to maintain the balance?

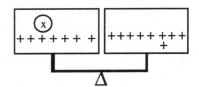

c) In part (b) you should have found that the scale balanced as shown at right.

This situation can be represented as x = 2. Is this the solution to the equation represented by the cups and tiles in part (a)?

d) Write an equation that represents the cups and tiles on the balance scale in part (a). Check to see if x = 2 is the solution to the equation in part (a) by replacing the x with 2 in the original equation.

MC-39. We want to solve the following algebra problem for x: x + 6 = 5x + 2. Use the resource page to complete the problem.

a) Draw the cups and tiles on the balance scale, then write the algebraic equation on the line.

b) Simplify the problem on the balance scale to figure out what is in each cup. Then explain your thinking.

c) What is the solution to the equation?

d) The final step is to check your work by substituting your solution into the original equation.

MC-40.   Use the resource page to solve the equation $2x + 3 = x + 7$.

   a)   Draw the picture and write the equation.

   b)   Simplify the problem on the balance scale to figure out what is in each cup, then explain in words what you did.

   c)   Now you have solved the equation. Check your solution by substituting the value you found into the original equation.

MC-41.   Use the resource page to solve the equation $x + 14 = 5x + 2$.

   a)   Draw the picture and write the equation.

   b)   Simplify the problem on the balance scale to figure out what is in each cup. Explain in words what you did.

   c)   Now you have solved the equation. Check your solution by substituting the value you found into the original equation.

MC-42.   Solve the following problems. Use the resource page to show your subproblems as well as how you checked your solution.

   a) $4x + 3 = 3x + 5$ b) $5x + 8 = 3x + 12$ c) $3x + 12 = 6x + 9$

MC-43.   Diedre did some trading and learned that two math club buttons plus a pencil would get her one set of markers. She also knew that one set of markers, two math club buttons, and a pencil would get her two reams of paper to make fliers announcing the t-shirt sale. She only wanted one ream of paper and had lots of markers. What did she have to trade to get one ream of paper? Use pictures or symbols to show your reasoning.

MC-44.   Solve the following equations using the cover-up method.

   a) $4x + 13 = 15$ b) $5x + 8 = 40$ c) $9x - 4 = 76$

   d) $3x + 11 = 13$ e) $18 + 7x = 4$ f) $20 - 6x = 2$

MC-45. Copy each diagram and complete the scale.

a)
-2.4   0.4

b)
$\frac{3}{4}$

$-\frac{1}{2}$

c)
$66\frac{2}{3}\%$

0%

MC-46. Draw and shade a picture to illustrate each number.

a) $\frac{4}{8}$ b) $\frac{3}{6}$ c) $\frac{5}{2}$

d) $1\frac{1}{5}$ e) $\frac{6}{5}$ f) $2\frac{1}{2}$

MC-47. Set up a Guess and Check table to solve the following problem. Write an equation. You may do this in either order.

Matt and Paul went on a fishing trip and caught 31 fish. Matt caught one less than three times as many fish as Paul caught. How many did each boy catch?

MC-48. Alisa went to the store to buy ribbon and bows. There were many colors to choose from. She decided to buy one white, three yellow, two green, and five blue bows for each box she has to wrap. Use the Distributive Property to show two different ways to calculate the total number of bows Alisa needs to buy if she has six boxes to wrap.

MC-49.   You have eight rectangles, two large squares, and six small squares on your desk. Your partner takes away one large square, five of the rectangles, and two of the small squares. Write an equation to express what happened and how many tiles you have left.

MC-50.   You are on a 650-mile trip by car. Your car used eight gallons of gas to travel the first 210 miles of the trip. If you stop at this point and fill the car's 18 gallon gas tank, will you make it the rest of the way? Show your work.

MC-51.   The Poppington family is returning home after a long car trip. Chad, Emily's younger brother, is annoying the family by constantly asking, "How long 'til we get home?" Emily notices the number 135 on the mileage marker at the side of the road (mileage markers on some highways indicate distance from the beginning of a highway or from a state line). The family will be home when they reach the mileage sign with the number 375. If the car is traveling at an average rate of 60 mph, then what is the answer to Chad's question? Write an equation, solve it, and answer the question using a complete sentence. Check your solution.

MC-52.   Frieda needs to earn $240 so she can go to Summer Camp. This is double the amount of money she has already saved. Write and solve an equation to find the amount of money Frieda has saved. Check your solution.

MC-53.   Ginger's gas tank holds 19 gallons. She fills the tank by adding 5 gallons. Use a variable to write an equation to find the number of gallons of gas in the tank before she filled it. Check your solution.

MC-54.   Solve the equation $2x + 9 = 4x + 5$ using the balance scales on your resource page.

    a)   Show the simplest way to keep the scales balanced.

    b)   Explain your reasoning in the "think clouds" and record the algebraic equations. Check your solution.

MC-55. Solve the equation $3x + 6 - 3 = 5x + 1$ using the balance scales on your resource page.

MC-56. As you use the resource page to do the problem, $4x + 1 = 3x - 1$, remember that adding a zero pair (+ and −) does not change the value of the equation or the balance.

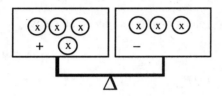

MC-57. Solve each of the equations below, then substitute your solution for x back into the original equation to be sure that your solution is correct.

a) $2x - 3 = 4x - 9$

b) $4x + 6 = 5x - 7$
     Remember that you can add an opposite to make zero pairs.

MC-58. Solve each of the following problems. Be sure to show all of the steps in each solution and substitute your solution for x back into the original equation. Notice that one of the pan diagrams below has positive (+) signs, while the other has negative (–) signs.

a)

b)

MC-59. Carlin and Jacob just finished the last problem.

Carlin: Hey, Jacob! I just noticed something. In that last problem you took three x's from each balance pan and got x – 2 = -3. Then all you have to do is use the cover-up method to finish the problem. You can just say x minus 2 is negative 3, so x has to be negative 1.

Jacob: You're right. Let's try that system for the next problems.

Solve the following equations for x. Show all steps.

a) $2x - 2 = 4x - 8$ b) $5x + 6 = 2x + 24$

c) $4x - 5 = 2x + 27$ d) $3x - 7 = 6x - 16$

MC-60. The perimeter of a rectangle is 48. The length is 8. Draw a diagram and solve the following equation to find the width: $48 = 2(8 + w)$.

MC-61. Find the value of each expression. Remember the order of operations.

a) $6^2 + 4 \cdot 5 \div 2$ b) $(6^2 + 4 \cdot 5) \div 2$ c) $(6^2 + 4) \cdot (5 \div 2)$

MC-62. Use the order of operations to complete these tables. Show all your work.

a)

x	y = 3 – 2x	y
-2	y = 3 – 2(-2)	
	y = 3 – (-4)	7
0		
2		
-1		
3		

b)

x	y = 1 – x²	y
-2	1 – (-2)²	
	1 – (4)	-3
-1		
2		
0		
1		

MC-63. Follow the instructions below for each problem.

a) How many one-fourths are in $4\frac{1}{4}$? Use your answer to rewrite $4\frac{1}{4}$ as a fraction with a denominator of 4.

b) How many one-thirds are in $3\frac{2}{3}$? Use your answer to rewrite $3\frac{2}{3}$ as a fraction with a denominator of 3.

c) How many one-eighths are in $5\frac{5}{8}$? Use your answer to rewrite $5\frac{5}{8}$ as a fraction with a denominator of 8.

d) How many one-fifths are in $6\frac{4}{5}$? Use your answer to rewrite $6\frac{4}{5}$ as a fraction with a denominator of 5.

MC-64. Answer the following questions. Write your answer as an equation.

a) Amber has to feed her pigs 36 gallons of molasses. How many pints is this?

b) Rufina walked to the mall and back home, a total of 4 miles. How many feet is this?

MC-65. Mr. Bennett's students took a math quiz and got the following scores: 8, 7, 5, 3, 4, 7, 2, 6, and 3.

a) What is the mean score?   b) What is the median score?

c) Is there a mode? What is it?   d) What is the range of these scores?

e) If the total possible were 8 points, calculate the <u>percentage</u> grades. Round to the nearest percentage.

f) Use the percentage scores to make a stem-and-leaf plot.

g) Use the percentage scores to make a box-and-whisker plot.

h) Which data display gives Mr. Bennett information for him to decide if most students understand the material on the quiz? Explain your thinking.

MC-66. Simplify: $\frac{4}{7} \div \frac{4}{5}$

(A) $1\frac{2}{5}$ (B) $\frac{5}{7}$ (C) $\frac{16}{35}$ (D) $\frac{8}{12}$ (E) none of these

MC-67. What is 15% of 80?

(A) 8   (B) 12   (C) 15   (D) 120   (E) none of these

MC-68. Explain how you found the correct answer in each of the preceding multiple choice questions.

MC-69. Follow your teacher's directions for practicing mental math. What strategy did you practice?

MC-70. David and Rozanne have the same amount of money. David has three envelopes labeled x and an additional $15, and Rozanne has four envelopes labeled x and an additional $9. All the envelopes contain the same amount of money. How much money must be in each envelope?

a) Write an equation to show that they have the same amount of money.

b) Solve your equation to see how much money is in an envelope.

MC-71. How much is each x worth? Explain how you know.

MC-72. The Mathematical Amusement Park is different from other amusement parks. Visitors encounter their first decision involving math when they pay their entrance fee. They have a choice between two plans. With Plan 1 they pay $5 to enter the park and $3 for each ride. With Plan 2 they pay $12 to enter the park and $2 for each ride.

a) Make a table like the one below to find the number of rides when the two plans cost the same.

Guess # Rides	Cost of Plan 1	Cost of Plan 2	Same (?)

b) Use x for the number of rides and write algebraic expressions for the cost of Plan 1 and for the cost of Plan 2.

c) Write an equation that shows when the plans cost the same amount.

d) Solve your equation and compare the result with the result from the table.

MC-73. Use the entries in your table from part (a) in the previous problem to set up and graph the two plans on the same set of axes.

a) Where does the line for Plan 1 cross the y-axis. Name this point with an ordered pair. Name the point where the line for Plan 2 crosses the y-axis. The point where a line crosses the y-axis is the **y-intercept**.

b) Label the coordinate of the place where the two lines intersect (cross).

c) What does the place where the lines intersect represent?

MC-74. After your day at the park you have some film to be
developed. Quick Photo Shop charges $2.25 plus
$0.05 per picture for developing and printing a roll of
film. The cost at Fast Photo Shop is $1.25 per roll
plus $0.09 for each picture.

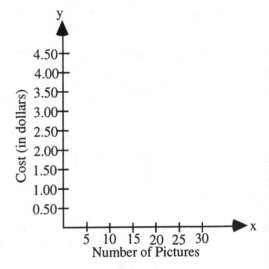

a) Use the resource page to create a table like the
one you made for the Mathematical Amusement
Park problem. Make guesses for the number of
pictures to see how the costs at the two photo
shops compare.

b) Graph the information from your table.
What is the y-intercept for each shop?

c) How does your graph help you decide
when the cost is the same?

d) Write algebraic expressions for each
shop. Set up the equation for when the
costs are the same. Solve the equation.

e) Are your answers in part (c) and part (d)
the same? Why or why not?

MC-75. Solve the following equations. Be sure to show your steps and check your answers.

a) $2x + 16 = 5x + 4$

b) $6 + 3x = 2x + 13$

c) $3x - 5 = 2x + 14$

d) $5x - 5 = x + 15$

e) $2x + 18 = 3 + 5x$

f) $4x + 6 = 7x - 15$

MC-76. Mental Math Clubs (MMC) have become popular at several schools. The Einstein Foundation, a charitable organization, awarded $2,000 to the Mental Math Club at Diedre's school. The money is to be spent for a dinner honoring MMC members from several schools. Diedre calls five local hotels that have banquet facilities to ask about the prices. She reserves the Perimeter Room at the Integer Inn. The cost is $500 to rent the room. The meals cost $12 per person. How many people can Diedre invite to the dinner? Write and solve an equation and then answer the question.

MC-77. Warner won a prize of $200 to use for a membership at a local health club. The cost to become a member is $65, and the monthly membership fee is $15. How long (in months) will it be until Warner starts paying the monthly membership fee (that is, until he runs out of prize money)? Write and solve an equation.

MC-78. Addison is on page 200 in the book he is reading. Five days ago he was on page 75. Assume he reads the same number of pages each day.

a) What is his reading rate? (That is, how many pages does he read per day?)

b) Copy and complete the table below.

Time (x) in days	-5	-4	-3	-2	-1	0	1	2	3
Amount (y)	75					200			

c) Write the rule.

d) When will he finish the book, which is 417 pages long?

e) When did he start reading the book?

f) Without graphing Addison's reading rate, name the point that represents the y-intercept.

MC-79. Simplify: $-5[(-2)(-3) + 9]$

(A) 75   (B) 15   (C) -15   (D) -75   (E) none of these

CHAPTER 5

MC-80.   Which of the following is equal to (0)(5)?

(A) $0 - 1$ (B) $\frac{2}{0}$ (C) $0 + 3$ (D) $\frac{0}{4}$ (E) none of these

MC-81.   Complete the following Diamond Problems.

Product   a)   b)   c)   d)   e)

Sum

MC-82.   Write an equation to find the perimeter of this rectangle.

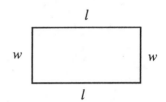

MC-83.   Consider the expression $3(x + 3)$.

a)   What does $3(x + 3)$ mean?

b)   You can represent $3(x + 3)$ with algebra tiles as shown below.

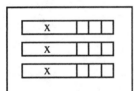

Draw three groups of $(x + 3)$.
You should see that this is $3x + 9$.

The Distributive Property allows us to rewrite a multiplication expression with parentheses as an equivalent expression without parentheses.

So $3(x + 3)$ may be rewritten as $3x + 9$.

c)   With your partner, use the Distributive Property to rewrite the following expressions and model them with algebra tiles.

i) $4(x + 2)$ ii) $2(x + 5)$ iii) $3(x + 4)$

MC-84.   Use the expression $3(x + 3)$ to answer the following questions.

a)   Can you solve this problem to find a number value for x?

b)   What happens if you make this problem $3(x + 3) = 21$? Can you solve for x?

c)   Look at part (b) above. Rewrite $3(x + 3)$ as $3x + 9$ to get the new equation, $3x + 9 = 21$. Solve for x.

MC-85.   Mario solved an equation and wants you to explain how he did it. Copy the solution steps he used. Next to each subproblem, give a mathematical reason that justifies how he got to the **next** subproblem. The first reason is given.

$4(2x + 5) = 5x + 32$	Use the Distributive Property to eliminate parentheses.
$8x + 20 = 5x + 32$	
$8x = 5x + 12$	
$3x = 12$	
$x = 4$	
$4(2 \cdot 4 + 5) = 5 \cdot 4 + 32$	
$4(13) = 52$	

MC-86.   Marisa left off parts of another problem and wants you to copy and complete it by filling in either the algebraic step or writing the reason that justifies <u>how to get to the next step</u> in the solution.

$7x + 5 = 4(3x - 5)$ _____

_____   Add 20 to both sides of the equation.

$7x + 25 = 12x$ _____

_____   Divide both sides by 5 to have one x.

$x = 5$ _____

$7 \cdot 5 + 5 = 4(3 \cdot 5 - 5)$ Use the order of operations to simplify each side.

$40 = 4(10)$ _____

MC-87.   Solve each equation. Show all subproblems.

a) $4(x + 2) = 28$ b) $2(x + 5) = 34$ c) $3(x + 4) = 30$

d) $2(x + 4) = 10$ e) $3(2x - 3) = 3$ f) $10x = 5(x + 8)$

g) $3(2x + 5) = 2x + 5$ h) $2(x - 4) = x - 7$

MC-88.   Simplify the following expressions.

a) $6(x + 3)$ b) $(2x - 4)3$ c) $-2(5x - 1)$

MC-89.   Write each expression in factored form using the Distributive Property.

  a)   8x + 12   b)   9x + 6   c)   -2x – 4

MC-90.   Solve each equation. Show your work.

  a)   24 = 2(x + 5)   b)   90 = (2x – 8)3

  c)   22 = 2(x + 4)   d)   3(2x – 1) = 9

MC-91.   Kendra notices the hard drive on her computer has
          42.6 MB available for storage. She estimates she
          fills up about 3 MB each month. Let x be the
          number of months until the storage space on the
          hard drive is filled up. Write an equation using x
          and solve it.

MC-92.   Use the Distributive Property to rewrite each expression in simplified form.

  a)   3(x + 6)   b)   x(x + 8)   c)   -6(7y + 4)

MC-93.   Follow the instructions for each problem.

  a)   How many one-fourths are in $2\frac{1}{4}$? Use your answer to rewrite $2\frac{1}{4}$ as a fraction
        with denominator of 4.

  b)   How many one-thirds are in $1\frac{1}{3}$? Use your answer to rewrite $1\frac{1}{3}$ as a fraction with
        a denominator of 3.

  c)   How many one-eighths are in $4\frac{5}{8}$? Use your answer to rewrite $4\frac{5}{8}$ as a fraction
        with a denominator of 8.

  d)   How many one-fifths are in $3\frac{2}{5}$? Use your answer to rewrite $3\frac{2}{5}$ as a fraction with
        a denominator of 5.

MC-94.   Tyler was working on another Target Game
          problem to stump his friends at school. His
          numbers were 2, 3, 4, 7, and 8. His target
          number was 6. Solve Tyler's problem.

MC-95. Doreen is at camp. She wants to call home to talk to her sister about the fun she is having there, but first she needs to talk to her parents. Her phone card has $2.50 left on it. The company charges $0.20 per minute. How long can she talk to her parents and still have five minutes to talk to her sister? Let t be the amount of time she can talk to her parents. Write an equation using t as the variable to answer Doreen's question. Use a Guess and Check table if you need it. Remember to write your answer as a sentence.

MC-96. Answer the following questions and explain your answers.

a) How would you divide nine granola bars evenly among three people?

b) How would you divide seven granola bars evenly among three people?

MC-97. Solve the following equations.

a) $4x = 12$

b) $3x + 2 = 11$

c) $2(x + 4) = 8$

d) $3(2x + 8) = 40$

e) $3(2x - 3) = 6$

MC-98. The Math Club is already planning a summer field trip. They have to choose between two amusement parks. Splash City charges $5.50 for admission plus $0.75 for each ride. The cost at Wet World is $2.00 admission plus $1.25 per ride.

a) For each park, define a variable and write an equation to show the relationship between the total cost and the number of rides.

b) Create a graph for the cost at each park and locate the point where the lines intersect. What is the significance of this point? Explain.

c) Name the y-intercept for both lines. What do these points represent?

d) Use your two equations to write an equation that shows when the total cost is the same for both parks. Solve the equation. Use algebra to check your answer.

e) For what number of rides is the total cost the same at both parks? What is that cost? Be sure to put your answer in a complete sentence.

f) When the club members were asked how many rides they planned to take, the mean was 8.2 and the median was 5. Which park should they choose? Explain your reasoning.

MC-99.   Use the Distributive Property or factor to rewrite each of the following expressions.

   a) $4(3x - 5)$

   b) $x \cdot y + x \cdot 8$

   c) $5 \cdot 2x + 5 \cdot 4 = \_\_ (\,\_\_ + \_\_\,)$

   d) $-(2x + 5)$

MC-100. Factor using the Distributive Property.

   a) $8x + 12$ b) $9x + 6$ c) $-2x - 4$

MC-101. Lynne took a taxicab from her office to the airport. She had to pay $3 per mile plus a $5 flat fee. Her total cost was $23. Write and solve an equation to find the number of miles she rode in the taxi. Write your answer in a complete sentence.

MC-102. Use the Distributive Property or factor to rewrite the following expressions.

   a) $(x + 7)5$ b) $7y - 56$ c) $-3(2x + 6)$ d) $15w - 10$

MC-103. Complete each spinner by calculating the value of the missing fraction.

   a)

   b)

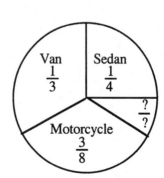

MC-104. Carmen and Ashley wanted to make egg sandwiches for their math class. They hard-boiled 30 eggs to use. While they were out jogging, Carmen's little brother Armand ate $\frac{2}{5}$ of the eggs.

   a)   How many eggs did Armand eat?   b)   What percent is this?

MC-105. The triangles in the grid at right show an example of a reflection or flip. Point A (-5, -1) reflected to A' = (5, -1), etc.

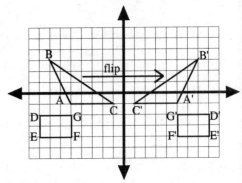

a) If B = (-7, 3) what are the coordinates of B'?

b) What is the line of symmetry for this entire graph?

c) What are the xy-coordinates of the reflected rectangle?

d) Are the rectangles congruent? Explain.

MC-106. Solve the following equations. Be sure to show your steps and check your answers.

a) $2(x + 4) = 32$

b) $3(2x - 2) = 12$

c) $21 = (x + 3)2$

d) $10(x - 3) = 100$

MC-107. Compute.

a) $-6 + (-7)$

b) $2 + (-8)$

c) $-3 - (-12)$

d) $7 \cdot (-5)$

e) $-5 + 15$

f) $4 - (-9)$

g) $37 + (-3)$

h) $-11 - (-23)$

i) $-36 \div 12$

j) $-8 \div (-8)$

MC-108. The Mental Math Club has not ordered the t-shirts yet. Diedre decided to call another t-shirt vendor. Her cousin told her about a place called *Tanks-A-Lot*, which charges a setup fee of $120 and an additional cost of $3 per shirt. Diedre needs to compare prices from the three different t-shirt venders: *Tanks-A-Lot, Teesers, and Screeners.*

a) Describe a way to compare the prices for the three companies.

b) Diedre has seen graphs that her mother prepared for her business presentations. She thinks a graph may be useful. Write an equation that represents the pricing for *Tanks-A-Lot*. Let x be the number of shirts and y be the total cost.

c) Complete the data table on the resource page.

Number of Shirts (x)	0	5	10	15	20	25	50
Total Cost (y)							

d) Graph the data in the table.

MC-109. Complete the table for *Teesers* and *Screeners*. Remember *Teesers* charged $78.00 for set up and $5.00 per shirt. *Screeners* charged $50.00 for set up and $7.00 per shirt.

a) Graph the *Teesers* and *Screeners* data on the same set of axes as *Tanks-A-Lot*. Use a ruler and make sure you use a different color for each line.

b) Identify the y-intercept for all 3 t-shirt vendors.

MC-110. Diedre does not know how many shirts she will need to order. Use the graphs to help Diedre decide which company she should select, depending on the size of the order.

a) Suppose Diedre wants to order 5 shirts. From what company should she order?

b) If Diedre orders 15 shirts, which company will be most economical?

c) If Diedre orders 45 shirts, which company will be most economical?

MC-111. The line representing *Teesers* crosses the line for *Tanks-A-Lot*. Write the coordinates of the point where the two lines cross. Write a few sentences explaining what this point represents.

MC-112. The cost equation for *Teesers* was $y = 78 + 5x$ and the cost equation for *Tanks-A-Lot* was $y = 3x + 120$. Write and solve one equation that will tell you the number of t-shirts when the cost for the two vendors is the same. Compare this with the result from your graph in the previous problem.

MC-113. The cost equation for *Screeners* was y = 50 + 7x. Use the same method as in the previous problem to write and solve one equation to find out when the price at *Teesers* will be the same as at *Screeners*. Compare this with the result from your equation in the previous problem.

MC-114. The line representing *Teesers* crosses the line for *Screeners*. Write the coordinates for the point where the two lines cross. Write a few sentences explaining what this point represents.

MC-115. Elle has moved to Hawksbluff for one year and wants to join a health club. She has narrowed her choices to two places: Thigh Hopes and ABSolutely fABulous. Thigh Hopes charges a fee of $95 to join and a monthly fee of $15. ABSolutely fABulous charges a fee of $125 to join and $12 per month. Which club should she join?

MC-116. Solve the following equations.

a) 12 = x – 7

b) 3x + (-4) = 2x + 9

c) 3x – 8 = 4x + (-2)

d) 2x – 6 = 1

e) 5x + 9 = 15

f) -16 = 7 + x

MC-117. **Lida's Luscious Waffles**—Makes enough for four people.

$1\frac{3}{4}$ cups flour

$\frac{1}{2}$ cups oil

$\frac{1}{16}$ cups baking powder

$1\frac{3}{4}$ cups milk

2   eggs

Rewrite the recipe to feed families of the following sizes. Use mixed numbers when fractions are greater than one.

a) 20 people

b) 10 people

c) 2 people

d) 14 people

MC-118. Answer the questions and follow the instructions below.

a) How many one-fifths are there in $2\frac{3}{5}$? Use your answer to write $2\frac{3}{5}$ as a fraction that is greater than one.

b) Rewrite the fraction $\frac{13}{8}$ as a mixed number.

c) How many one-thirds are there in $4\frac{2}{3}$? Use your answer to write $4\frac{2}{3}$ as a fraction that is greater than one.

d) Rewrite the fraction $\frac{15}{4}$ as a mixed number.

MC-119.

MIXED NUMBERS

The number $4\frac{1}{4}$ is called a **MIXED NUMBER** because it is made from a whole number, 4, and a fraction, $\frac{1}{4}$. It is a mix of a whole number and a fraction:

$$4\frac{1}{4} = \frac{16}{4} + \frac{1}{4} = \frac{17}{4}$$

The number $\frac{17}{4}$ is a fraction that is greater than 1 because the numerator is greater than the denominator. Sometimes fractions that are greater than one are called "improper fractions." "Improper" does not mean wrong. For mathematics, keeping a fraction in its "improper form" is often more useful than changing it to a mixed number.

Make these notes in your Tool Kit to the right of the double-lined box.

a) Describe how to change a whole number into a fraction with a denominator greater than one.

b) List one example in mathematics where keeping a fraction in its improper form is more useful than changing it to a mixed number.

MC-120.

Chapter Summary It is time to summarize and review what you have learned in this chapter. Work with your partner or study team.

a) Make a list of the different ways you learned to solve equations in this chapter. Discuss the list with other team members and revise it if necessary.

b) Choose four equations from the chapter that represent the ways you learned to solve equations and progress from easier to more difficult. Copy the equations and show how to solve them.

MC-121. Use the models of balance scales below to complete parts (a) and (b).

a) Write an algebraic equation for each balance scale.

b) Solve each equation.

MC-122. Solve the following equations for x. Draw the balance scale if needed.

a) $2x + 1 = 15$

b) $5x + 14 = x + (-2)$

c) $2x - 1 = 5x + 8$

d) $4x = 28 + 2x$

e) $-24 = 4x - 10$

f) $5x + 3 = 15x + (-13)$

MC-123. Vicky is a high school student who repairs computers and computer networks. She charges $68 for the first hour and $28 for each additional hour of work.

a) Write an algebraic expression to represent how much Vicki charges for x hours.

b) The summer camp hired Vicky to work on computers. The camp received a bill from her that totaled $236. How many hours did Vicky work? Write an equation, solve it, and answer the question.

MC-124. Darren started folding newspapers 20 minutes before Selina arrived. By the time she arrived, he had folded 200 newspapers.

a) How many newspapers can Darren fold per minute?

b) After she arrived, Selina decided to help Darren. She can fold 15 papers per minute. How long will it be until Darren and Selina have folded the same number of newspapers?

c) If you did not use an equation in part (b), write an equation to show how many minutes it will take Selina to fold as many papers as Darren. Let m stand for the number of minutes.

MC-125. Solve the following equations. Draw a balance scale, if needed.

a) $-12 = 5x - 7$

b) $5(x + 1) = -10$

c) $15 + x = 10 + 5x$

d) $(x + 2)3 = x + (-4)$

e) $2[x + (-5)] = 12$

f) $4x + 7 = (x - 7)2$

MC-126. Use the order of operations and substitution to complete these tables. In part (b), remember to square x, then subtract.

a)

x	y = 5 – x	y
-2	y = 5 – (-2)	7
1		
0		
2		
-1		
3		
4		

b)

x	y = 5 – x²	y
-2		
3		
-1	y = 5 – (-1)² y = 5 – (1)	
2		
-3		
0		
1		

MC-127. Graph the two equations in the previous problem on the same set of axes.

a) How are the graphs and equations alike?

b) How are they different?

MC-128. Complete the following Diamond Problems.

Product

Sum

a)

b)

c)

d)

e)

MC-129. Tom is buying new computers for his writing team. He can buy the first five at a dealer discount. The other fifteen will be purchased for an extra $50 each. The cost of the computers comes to a grand total of $11,750. Find how much each of the discounted computers cost. A Guess and Check table might be useful. Write an equation.

MC-130. **What We Have Done in This Chapter**

Below is a list of the Tool Kit entries from this chapter.

- MC-8   Equations
- MC-119   Mixed Numbers

Review all the entries and read the notes you made in your Tool Kit. Make a list of any questions, terms, or notes you do not understand. Ask your partner or study team members for help. If anything is still unclear, ask your teacher.

GLOSSARY

absolute value: (||) The distance of a number from zero on the number line. It is always non-negative. (53)

acute angle: An angle with a measure greater than 0° and less than 90°.

acute triangle: A triangle with all three angle measures less than 90°.

addition: (+) An operation that tells how many objects there are when two sets are combined. The result is the number of objects in the two sets together, called a sum. In arithmetic, the word "object" usually means "number." (49)

adjacent angles: Angles which share a common side and vertex but no common interior points.

algebra: A branch of mathematics that uses variables to generalize the rules of numbers and numerical operations.

algebraic expression: Variables and constants, joined by addition or subtraction. Examples: $3x$ or $2x + 4$ (129)

algorithm: A fixed rule for carrying out a mathematical procedure. Example: To find the average of a set of values, find their sum and divide by the number of values.

altitude of a triangle (height): The perpendicular distance from a vertex to the opposite side (or its extension) of a triangle.

angle: A geometric figure made up of two rays or line segments that have the same endpoint.

angle bisector: A ray that divides an angle into two congruent parts. (409)

arc: The portion of a circle between two points on a circle. (408)

area: The measure in square units of the interior region of a plane figure or the surface of a three-dimensional figure. (156)

area of a triangle: To find the area of a triangle, multiply the length of the base (b) by the height (h) and divide by two. $A = \frac{1}{2} bh$ (221)

area of a circle: $A = \pi r^2$, where r is the length of the radius of the circle. See area. (225)

associative property for addition: Changing the grouping of the numbers does not change the result in addition. Example: $(5 + 3) + 7 = 5 + (3 + 7)$ (402)

associative property for multiplication: Changing the grouping of the numbers does not change the result in multiplication. Example: $(5 \cdot 3) \cdot 2 = 5 \cdot (3 \cdot 2)$ (402)

average (mean): The sum of given numbers divided by the number of numbers used in computing the sum. Example: The average of 1, 4, and 10 is $(1 + 4 + 10) \div 3 = 5$. (14)

axis (pl. axes): A number line which can be used to indicate a position of a point, based on its coordinates. (28)

base of an exponent: The number used as the factor in an exponential expression. Example: $5^2 = 5 \cdot 5$. The number 5 is the base. (298)

base: For a triangle, the base may be any side, although usually it is the bottom one. For a trapezoid, the two parallel sides are the bases. For a cylinder or prism, either one of the two congruent parallel faces may be the base while for a pyramid or cone, the base is the (flat) face which does not contain the vertex (where all the sides come together). (215, 221, 309)

bimodal: A set of numbers that has two modes. (18)

box-and-whisker plot: A graphic way of showing a summary of data using the median, quartiles, and extremes of the data. (27)

certainty: When an event will definitely happen. The probability of a certain event is 1.

center: (or center point) The point equidistant from all points on a circle. (407)

central angle: An angle whose vertex is the center of a circle. (410)

chord: A line segment that connects two points on a circle. (410)

circle: The set of all points in two dimensions that are the same distance r from a fixed point P. The fixed point P is called the center of the circle and the distance r is called the radius. (222)

circumference: The distance around the outside of a circle. You can calculate circumference from the diameter (d) or the radius (r). $C = \pi d = 2\pi r$. (225)

coefficient (numerical): The numeral part of a term, such as 6 in 6x. (260)

combining like terms: When working with an expression, terms that are exactly the same except for their coefficients can be combined into one quantity. Terms are combined by addition and subtraction of the coefficients. Example: $3x^2 + 2y + 6 + 4y - 2x^2 = x^2 + 6y + 6$. (141)

common: Shared. (159)

common factor: A common term factor: (1) in arithmetic, the integers multiplied are called factors; (2) in algebra, a monomial or polynomial that is a factor of a polynomial.
For example: $10x + 15 = 5(2x + 3)$. Five is the common factor. (159)

common multiple: A number that is a multiple of the two or more numbers. Example: 24 and 48 are common multiples of 3 and 8. (86)

commutative property: The property of an operation such that changing the order of the numbers does not change the result of the operation. Examples: $3 \cdot 4 = 4 \cdot 3$ or $7 + 8 = 8 + 7$

compass and straightedge (construction with): A geometric construction. The straightedge is only used to draw line segments. The compass is used to transfer equal distances and draw arcs and circles. (407)

complementary angles: Two angles whose sum is 90°.

complementary probabilities: Two probabilities are complementary if their sum is one.

complex fraction: A fraction with a fraction in the numerator and/or the denominator.

composite figure: A shape made of several simpler figures.

composite number: A number with more than two factors.

compound interest: Interest paid on both the principal and previous interest earned which accumulates over time. It can be calculated by using the formula $B = p(1 + r)^t$, where B is the balance, p is the principal, r is the annual rate, and t is the time in years the account earns interest. (265)

cone: A three dimensional figure with one circular base and one vertex. (375)

congruent: Figures which have the same size and shape. (207)

conjecture: An educated guess based on data, patterns, and data. Scientists use the term hypothesis.

consecutive: In order. Example: 8, 9, 10 are consecutive numbers. (10)

constant: A numerical term which does not change.

coordinate: See ordered pair.

coordinate grid (system): A two dimensional system formed by two perpendicular number lines that intersect at their zero points. The location of a point is given by first stating the horizontal location (x) and then the vertical location (y), written as an ordered pair, (x, y). (28)

correlation: A measure of interdependence of two sets of data. (33)

corresponding parts: Points, edges (sides), or angles in congruent or similar figures that are arranged in similar ways. For instance if $\triangle ABC$ is similar to $\triangle DEF$, then side AB corresponds to side DE and angle C corresponds to angle F. (229)

cross multiplication: A way to find a missing numerator or denominator in equivalent fractions by multiplying diagonally across the equal sign to get an equivalent equation without fractions. Example: In $\frac{a}{b} = \frac{c}{d}$, after cross multiplication the equation would be $ad = bc$. (212)

cube: A rectangular prism with 6 congruent faces, all squares.

cubic unit: A cube each of whose edges measures 1 unit in length. Volume is measured in cubic units. (293)

cylinder: Commonly, a three dimensional object with two circular, congruent, and parallel bases. (319)

decimal point: The dot separating the ones and tenths places in a decimal number.

denominator: The lower part of a fraction which tells into how many equal parts the whole is divided. (108)

dependent events: Two events are dependent if the outcome of the first event affects the outcome of the second event.

diagonal: A segment that joins two vertices of a polygon and is not one of the sides.

diameter: A line segment that has its endpoints on the circle and passes through the center. The longest chord in a circle. (222)

difference: The answer to a subtraction problem. (58)

digit: One of the ten numerals: 0, 1, 2, 3, 4, 5, 6, 7, 8, 9.

distributive property: For any a, b, and c, a(b + c) = ab + ac.
Example: $10(7 + 2) = 10 \cdot 7 + 10 \cdot 2$ (159)

dividend: A quantity to be divided. See divisor.

divisible: A number is divisible by another if their remainder is zero.

division: The inverse operation to multiplication. The operation which creates equal groups. (75)

divisor: The quantity by which another quantity is to be divided. dividend ÷ divisor = quotient (262)

dodecagon: A polygon with 12 sides. (411)

edge: The line segment where two faces of a solid figure meet. (369)

endpoint: Either of the two points which mark the ends of a line segment. (409)

enlargement ratio: The ratio of similarity comparing a figure to a similar larger one is often called the enlargement ratio. This number tells you by what factor the first figure is enlarged to get the second.

equal: Having the same value.

equal ratios: Two equivalent fractions; a proportion. (208)

equation: A mathematical sentence relating two mathematical expressions with an equal sign (=). (173)

equilateral triangle: A triangle with all three sides the same length. (408)

equivalent: Naming the same amount with a different name. (91)

evaluate (an expression): To evaluate an expression, substitute the value(s) given for the variable(s) and perform the operations according to the order of operations. (129)

even number: A whole number which is divisible by two with no remainder.

event: One or more results of an experiment.

exponent: In the expression 2^5, 5 is called the exponent. The exponent indicates how many times to use the base as a multiplier. (298)

expression: See algebraic expression.

face: A flat side of a three-dimensional figure. (309)

factor: When two or more numbers are multiplied, each of the numbers multiplied is a factor of the product. (158)

factored form: The result of writing an algebraic expression as a product.
Example: $4x^3 + 12x^2 + 8x = 4x(x + 1)(x + 2)$ (137)

formula: An equation that shows a mathematical relationship. (279)

fraction: A number expressed in the form $\frac{a}{b}$ where a and b are integers and b is not equal to 0. (4)

frequency: The number of times something occurs in an interval or in a data set.

graph: A visual display of information in an organized manner. (6)

greatest common factor (GCF): The largest number which will divide evenly into two or more numbers. Example: 6 is the greatest common factor of 12 and 18.

guess and check table: A problem solving strategy in which you begin by making a guess and then check whether or not your answer is correct. In the process of checking, you gain information about how close your guess might be and make adjustments to your guess. Being organized is crucial to the success of this method, as well as writing a usable table. Guess and check leads to writing equations to represent word problems. (15)

height (altitude): The perpendicular distance between two bases, or between a vertex and a base. See altitude. (215)

hexagon: A polygon with six sides. (411)

horizontal: Parallel to the horizon. The x-axis in a coordinate grid is the horizontal axis. (45)

hypotenuse: In a right triangle, the longest side of the triangle, opposite the right angle, is called the hypotenuse. (291)

identity property of addition: Zero is the identity for addition. It does not change the value of a number when added to the number. (401)

identity property of multiplication: One is the identity element for multiplication. Multiplying by one does not change the value of a number. (93)

impossibility: An event with a probability of zero.

independent events: Two events are independent if the outcome of the second event does not depend on the outcome of the first event.

inequality: A mathematical sentence which compares two quantities, showing they are not the same. The symbols used may be: < (less than), > (greater than), to), or ≠ (not equal to). (69)

integers: The set of numbers { . . .,-3, -2, -1, 0, 1, 2, 3,... } (49)

intersect: To meet or cross. The intersection of two sets consists of all the points or elements that belong to both sets.

interval: A set of numbers between two given numbers.

inverse operations: An operation that undoes another operation. Example: Multiplication is the inverse operation for division. (295)

irrational numbers: Numbers that cannot be written as the ratio of two integers. (225)

isosceles triangle: A triangle with at least two sides equal in length.

least common multiple (LCM): The smallest common multiple of set of two or more numbers. Example: The least common multiple of 4 and 6 is 12. (86)

leg of a right triangle: Either of the two shorter sides of a right triangle. (291)

like terms: Terms that have the same variable part and corresponding exponent. 5 and 19 are like terms, 3xy and 5xy are like terms, $6x^2$ and $-3x^2$ are like terms. (141)

line: An infinite set of points forming a straight path extending in two directions. (12)

line segment: A part of a line between two endpoints. (407)

linear equation: An equation whose graph is a line, generated by an equation with a linear expression in it. (344)

linear expression: An expression in the form of ax + b, where a and b are numbers.

literal equation: An equation with two or more variables. (250)

lower quartile: The median of the lower half of an ordered set of data is the lower quartile. (27)

lowest common denominator (LCD): The smallest common multiple of the denominators of two or more fractions. Example: The LCD of $\frac{5}{12}$ and $\frac{3}{8}$ is 24.

mean: A measure of central tendency often referred to as the average. See average. (26)

measure of central tendency: Mean, median, and mode are all measures of central tendency, reflecting specific statistical information about a set of data. (26)

median: The middle number of a set of ordered data. If there is no distinct middle, the average of the two middle numbers is the median. (26)

midpoint: The point on a line segment that divides the line segment into two congruent line segments. (409)

mixed number (fraction): A number with an integer component and a fraction component. Example: $2\frac{3}{4}$ (199)

mode: The number or numbers that occur the most often in a set of data. There can be more than one mode. (26)

multiple: The product of a whole number and any other (nonzero) whole number. Example: 15 is a multiple of 5.

multiplication: An operation which reflects repeated addition. Example: $3 \cdot 4 = 4 + 4 + 4$. (71)

natural numbers: The counting numbers beginning with one. Example: 1, 2, 3... (49)

negative correlation: A relationship between two sets of variables in which one generally increases as the other decreases. (33)

negative numbers: Numbers which are less than zero, designated with a $-$ sign. (49)

negative slope: Lines that slant downward from left to right showing a negative ratio when comparing the vertical change to the horizontal change. (339)

net: A two dimensional one-piece plan which can be folded into a three dimensional shape. (321)

non-linear: A set of points which do not lie on a straight line when connected.

number line: A diagram representing all real numbers as points on a line. (12)

numeral: An expression (which is not a variable) that names a particular number.

numerator: The number above the bar in a fraction which tells the number of parts in relationship to the number of parts in the whole. (91)

obtuse angle: An angle whose measure is greater than 90° and less than 180°.

octagon: A polygon with eight sides. (411)

odd number: An integer which cannot be evenly divided by two. (34)

operation: In mathematics, addition, subtraction, multiplication, division, raising to a power and taking a root are operations.

order of operations: Rules which define in what sequence operations will be completed when an expression is presented for evaluation. Expressions inside parentheses are evaluated first, then multiplication or division (left to right) followed by addition and subtraction (left to right). Exponents are a form of multiplication. (131)

origin: The point assigned to zero on the number line or the point where the x- and y-axes intersect in a coordinate system. (28)

ordered pair: A pair of numbers (a, b) used to indicate a position on a coordinate plane. The first number indicates the horizontal coordinate; the second number indicates the vertical coordinate. Syn: coordinate. (28)

outcome: Possible result in an experiment or consequence of an action. (85)

outlier: A number in a set of data that is much larger or much smaller than the other numbers in the set. (14)

parabola: A graph of the equation $y = ax^2 + bx + c$ with $a \neq$ zero. (79)

parallel: ($\parallel$) Two straight lines on a two-dimensional surface which never intersect and are the same distance apart are said to be parallel. (215)

parallelogram: A quadrilateral with opposite sides parallel. (215)

pentagon: A polygon with five sides.

percent: (%) A ratio that compares a number to 100. (119)

perfect square: The product of an integer times itself gives a perfect square. Examples: 1, 4, and 9 are perfect squares because $1 = 1 \cdot 1$; $4 = 2 \cdot 2$; $9 = 3 \cdot 3$; $16 = 4 \cdot 4$... (298).

perimeter: The distance around a figure on a flat surface. (11)

perpendicular: ($\perp$) Lines, segments, or rays that intersect to form right angles.

perpendicular bisector: A line, ray, or segment that divides a segment into two congruent segments and is perpendicular to the segment. (409)

pi (π): The ratio of a circle's circumference to its diameter. An irrational number, it is common to use the approximation of 3.14 or $\frac{22}{7}$ if you are not using a scientific calculator with a π key. (223)

place value: The value of a position of a digit in a number.

plane: A flat surface that extends infinitely in all directions. It has no thickness.

point: An exact location in space. In two dimensions, an ordered pair specifies a point in a coordinate plane. (28)

polygon: A two-dimensional closed figure made of straight line segments (sides or edges) connected end to end (at vertices). The segments may not cross. Examples: triangle or quadrilateral. (309)

polyhedron: A three-dimensional figure with no holes in which all faces are polygons.

population: A collection of objects or group of people about whom information is gathered.

positive correlation: A relationship between two sets of variables in which one generally increases as the other increases. (33)

positive slope: Lines that slant upwards from left to right showing a positive ratio when comparing the vertical change to the horizontal change of the line. (339)

positive numbers: Numbers that are greater than zero.

power (exponent): See exponent.

prime: A number with exactly two factors. Examples: 2, 3, 5, 7...

prime factorization: The expression of a number as the product of prime factors.

prism: A three-dimensional figure composed of polygonal faces and two parallel, congruent faces called bases. No holes are permitted in the solid. The remaining faces are parallelograms (or rectangles). A prism is named for the shape of its base. (309)

probability: The chance of an event happening. When the outcomes are equally likely, it equals the number of event outcomes divided by the total number of outcomes. Example: when rolling a number cube, the probability that you will roll a 3 is: $\frac{1 \text{ way}}{6 \text{ possible outcomes}} = \frac{1}{6}$. (85)

product ($\cdot$): Result of multiplying. Example: 72 is the product of $8 \cdot 9$. (71)

proportion: An equation of two equivalent ratios. Example: $\frac{1}{3} = \frac{3}{9}$ (208)

pyramid: A polyhedron with a polygonal base and whose other faces are triangles with a common vertex. A pyramid is named for the shape of its base.

Pythagorean Theorem: The sum of the squares of the lengths of the legs of a right triangle is equal to the square of the length of the hypotenuse. (294)

quadrants: The four sections of a coordinate grid. (46)

quadrilateral: A polygon with four sides.

quartile: Along with the median, the quartiles divide a set of data into four groups of the same size. (27)

quotient: The result of a division problem. (74)

radius: (plural: **radii**) The distance from the center to a point on the circle. (225)

random sample: A sample in which each item in the population or sample space has an equal chance of being selected.

range: In statistics, the difference between the least and greatest values in the data set. (14)

rate: A ratio comparing two quantities, often a comparison of time. Example: miles per hour. (337)

rate of change: see slope (337)

ratio: A comparison of two numbers which can indicate division. It can be written three ways: 2 boys to 5 girls, 2 boys : 5 girls, or $\frac{2 \text{ boys}}{5 \text{ girls}}$. (207)

ratio of similarity: The ratio of similarity between any two similar figures is the ratio of any pair of corresponding sides. In this course ratios will always be listed in the order that compares the "new" to the "original" figure. This ratio is also known as the enlargement or reduction factor in this course. (233)

rational number: A number that can be written in the form $\frac{a}{b}$ with a and b integers and $b \neq$ zero.

ray: A portion of a line that has one endpoint and extends forever in one direction.

real numbers: The set of rational and irrational numbers. (All the numbers on the number line.)

reciprocals: Two numbers which have a product of 1. Example: 2 and $\frac{1}{2}$ are reciprocals of each other. (256)

rectangle: A quadrilateral with four right angles. Its two pairs of opposite sides are parallel and congruent. (11)

reduce: To put a fraction into simplest form. (99)

regular polygon: A polygon in which all sides are congruent and all angles have the same measure.

representative sample: A subset (group) of a given population with the same characteristics as the population.

rhombus: A quadrilateral with four congruent sides.

right angle: An angle whose measure is 90°. (291)

right triangle: A triangle with one right angle in it. (291)

root: A number that can be used as a factor a given number of times. Example: The square root of 16 is 4 because $4 \cdot 4 = 16$. $\sqrt{16} = 4$ (298)

scale factor: A ratio between two sets of measurements. (229)

scale (scaling): An arrangement of numbers in uniform intervals. (12)

scalene triangle: A triangle with no two sides of equal length.

scatter plot: Two related sets of data graphed as points, often in a coordinate plane. See positive and negative correlation. (30)

scientific notation: A method of writing very large or very small numbers as a product of a power of ten and a number greater than or equal to one and less than 10. Example: $124,500 = 1.245 \cdot 10^5$ (386)

sector: A part of the interior of a circle bounded by two radii and the arc between their endpoints.

semi-circle: Half of a circle.

set: A collection of items. (313)

similar figures: Figures which are similar have the same shape but not necessarily the same size. The lengths of the corresponding sides are proportional to one another; the corresponding angles are congruent. (229)

simple interest: Interest paid only on the principal (the amount invested). It is found by multiplying the principal, the rate, and the time in years. (265)

simplest form of a fraction: A fraction whose numerator and denominator have no common factor greater than one. (99)

simplify: To combine like terms; to express the quantity using as few symbols as possible; to put a fraction in lowest terms. (99, 106)

slope: A way to specify the steepness of a line defined as the ratio of the vertical distance divided by the horizontal distance between any two points on the line. (339)

solution: Any value for a variable that makes an equation true. (176)

square: A quadrilateral with four congruent sides and four right angles. (410)

square number: Any number which is the product of two identical integers. Examples: $1 \cdot 1 = 1$, $2 \cdot 2 = 4$, $3 \cdot 3 = 9$ ... (298)

square root: See root.

square measure: The units used to describe the measure of an area in the form of 1 x 1 unit squares. (293)

stem and leaf plot: A frequency distribution made by arranging the data. (19)

straight angle: An angle whose measure is 180°.

subproblems: A problem solving strategy which breaks a problem into smaller parts which must be solved in order to solve the original, complex problem. (304)

substitution: Replacing one symbol by another (a number, a variable, or other algebraic expression) without changing the value of the expression.

subtraction (-): An operation that gives the difference between two numbers. (57)

sum: An answer to a addition problem. (49)

supplementary angles: Two angles whose measurements give a sum of 180°.

surface area: The total area of all faces and bases of a polyhedron, cylinder, cone, or pyramid. (315)

term: Each part of the expression separated by addition or subtraction signs is a term. (131)

tetrahedron: A polyhedron with four faces.

tick mark: An indicator that a number line has been divided into intervals of equal length. (46)

trimodal: A set of data that has three modes. (18)

truncate: To cut off or shorten.

trapezoid: A quadrilateral with exactly one pair of parallel sides. (221)

triangle: A polygon with three sides. (221)

unit price: The cost of one item or one measure of an item. Example: cost for one pound or one gallon.

unit rate: A rate with a denominator of one.

units digit: The numeral in the ones place.

upper quartile: The median of the upper half of an ordered set of data. (140)

variable: A symbol or letter that represents a number. (140)

vertex: The point at which two rays, line segments, or lines meet.

vertical: At right angles to the horizon. In a coordinate grid, the y-axis runs vertically. (45)

vertical angles: The angles opposite each other when two lines intersect.

volume: The number of cubic units inside a three dimensional object. (311)

x-axis: The horizontal number line on a coordinate grid. (28)

x-intercepts: The point(s) where a graph intersects the x-axis. An x-intercept always has coordinates (x, 0). (54)

y-axis: The vertical number line on a coordinate grid. (28)

y-intercepts: The point(s) where a graph intersects the y-axis. The y-intercept always has coordinates (0, y). (54)

INDEX

Chapter Prefixes

Many of the page numbers listed here contain the definitions or examples of the topic listed. It may be necessary, however, to read text on preceding pages or the pages following to understand the topic fully. Also, on some page numbers listed here you will find "good examples" of the topic, but they may not offer any explanation. It is very important, therefore, for you to be sure you correct and complete your homework and keep it organized. Your record of the problems related to these topics may be your best index to understanding the mathematics of this course.